THE DONEGAL WONDER BOOK

SOME SEUMAS MACMANUS BOOKS

The Young Prince Mounted
the Winged Horse ~

William Stevens

THE DONEGAL
WONDER BOOK

By

SEUMAS MACMANUS

NEW YORK
FREDERICK A. STOKES COMPANY
MCMXXVI

To
MARIQUITA AND PATRICIA
THE MOST FAITHFUL, MOST EAGER AND PERSISTENT, AND
ALWAYS MOST UNSATISFIED, AUDIENCE, THAT THIS SHANACHIE
EVER FASCINATED WITH HIS FAIRY TALES, THE BOOK OF
WONDER STORIES IS LOVINGLY INSCRIBED.

CONTENTS

THE TALES

Here's just a little handful of bloom from Donegal's teeming garden of thousand-year-old tales—tales of magic, mystery, witchery, and færie—whose riotous profusion filled with fragrance all my childhood days: whether by my father's fireside in Tanatalan, in the little thatched school of Glen Cuach, on the brown braes of the Bearna Dearg and green banks of Inver, or amid the lone moors of Meenawanna.

Peace to the ashes of a score of now silent *Shanachies,** my masters, who fondly treasured these story-flowers, and were forever scattering them in the paths of our children, and with them bewitching and refreshing the myriad hungering hearts around the turf-fires on the hundred hills of Banagh. Green be their memories, and on their noble breasts light lie the heathery quilt! Sweet peace to the souls, especially, of the Princes of all that halöed company—thou, O rare John O'Cuinn! and thou, O rarest Shan O'Hegarty!—who now in Heaven hold crowding hosts of wide-eyed angels, and child-heart saints, entranced with your Wonder Tales of Donegal.

*Story-tellers.

THE WONDERS OF THE THREE
DONALS

DONAL O'DONNELL was an able farming man who did a small bit of farming and a small bit of shepherding, and a small bit of trading at fairs —and he, with his wife Sorcha, lee-and-long miles from all neighbors, lived in the wild mountain Gap of Barnesmor in Donegal. No place was too wild for him, for he'd grown sour at the world, and taken a mighty dislike to all men—which led him an unhappy life.

There was a morning in the wintertime, and Donal got up before the screek of day; and, gathering with him a couple of score head of sheep, traveled out over the hills for Brockagh Fair, for to sell them. But, if he went out, he didn't cross the threshold till he first left severe warnings on his wife Sorcha, as was usual with him, to be certain sure and allow no streelers nor strollers, vagrants nor vagabonds, to stop and take lodgings there—for Donal set small store on this kind of gentry. Sorcha, she promised.

Now, it wasn't a good day when Donal started, and it's little better, but worse, it got as the day wore on; and the sleet that come down in the evening would drive through a door, you'd think —it was that sharp and bitter, and pelting so hard. And it would make the heart of a stone on the face of the mountain melt, for thinkin' of any poor homeless one that would be abroad in Barnesmor Gap upon an evening such.

Just at dayligone (twilight), Sorcha, who was doing little *timerishes* within the house, and sweeping up the hearth in front of a bright fire, heard a *tindherara* upon the door, and, going to it and opening it, found there a poor, shivering old man with a pack on his back. And, "The blessing of God be on this house and all in it," says he. "I'm a poor packman, and I'm storm-stayed in the Gap, and I'd be obliged if you'd give me a night's lodgin'."

Sorcha, she tried for to raise all the objections in the world; but the night was so cruel and

2

Sorcha had such a soft heart, and the poor old packman pleaded so hard, and looked so pitiful, that she hadn't the heart in her for to shut him out in the storm, so she said, "You can come in and get a heat of the fire into your bones till my man Donal is near comin' home, anyhow."

The old peddler thanked her, and prayed God to bless her; and came in, and made himself at home in the chimney-corner.

Not long seated was he till there was another *tindherara* beaten on the door; and, behold you! when Sorcha opened it, wasn't there another old man with a pack on his back, too, and he shivering and asking shelter from the storm, and a night's lodging, for God's sake. Well, poor Sorcha argued with him stiff; but, as she wasn't able to pluck up heart for to shut him out entirely, she bade him come in and get the fire into his bones afore Donal's time of comin'. And he came in and made himself at home in the other chimney-corner.

Lo and behold ye! not well seated was this second peddler till a third *tindherara* was heard on the door; and there was still another peddler begging shelter from the storm and a night's lodging, for heaven's sake. And, to make a long story short, Sorcha couldn't help but let him walk in also—that he might get a heat of the fire atween then and Donal's homecomin'. She warned them to make the most of their time, for that her man Donal heartily disliked all men—in particular, streelers and strollers of all sorts—couldn't bear them in his house, and would make fearsome scatterment of them if he found them. Plump in front of the fire this third man settles himself; and there the three of them sat, with their packs at their sides, every man of them smoking, and reeking great clouds, that you wouldn't know most which the smoke came from—their pipes or their sleet-steeped duds.

By-and-by there comes to the door another *tindherara,* far louder and wickeder than any yet; and when Sorcha heard it, and went and drew the bolt, who should step in but Donal himself, before he was expected! The look that come on Donal's face as he looked from one to the other of the three old peddlers, and seen what was before him, was a caution!

Says he to Sorcha, "I thought, my good woman, I warned you, before crossing the threshold this

mornin', to give house-room neither to streelers
nor strollers; and is this how you've obeyed me?"

Poor Sorcha, she pleaded that, much as she
wished to obey him, she hadn't it in her heart to
turn away a dog upon such a night, let alone a
Christian, and that she had only given them leave
to come in and get a bit of heat in their bones
atween their coming and his.

This mollified Donal but little: and he gave the
three peddlers, he said, just a quarter of an hour
to turn themselves at the fire, and do the other
side, afore startin'.

They thanked him; and then he pulled forward
a chair to the fire himself, and he lit his pipe
and put speak on them; and he asked the first of
them, him in the far chimney-corner, what his
name was and what was he to trade.

"Donal O'Sheary by name, if it please you,"
says the old man, replying, "and I'm a peddler to
trade."

"And what's your name?" says Donal O'Donnell, says he to the old man in the other chimney-
corner, "and what's your followin'?"

"Donal O'Neary by name," says he, "and I follow peddlin' for a trade."

"And your name?" says he to the man in the middle, beside himself, "and your profession?"

"Peddlin' is my profession," says he straight back, "and Donal O'Leary my name."

"Well, well, well, well!" says Donal O'Donnell, says he, "if that isn't the quarest thing ever I heard tell of within my lifetime; and I'm a middling old man now! Here's three peddlers of you come in, every one independent of the other, to my house in my absence; and every one of you is named Donal, and I Donal myself! If a quarer thing than that ever happened before, I'd travel a good bit to shake hands on the man who met up with it."

"Troth and," said the first old man, Donal O'Sheary, says he, "maybe it isn't far you'd have to go for that same."

"What do you mean?" says Donal O'Donnell, says he.

"I mane to say that I met with as quare myself—and quarer."

"I don't believe you," says Donal O'Donnell.

"And what will you owe me if I prove you mistaken?" says Donal O'Sheary.

6

"The sweetest of a supper and the softest of a bed," says the man of the house.

"Good!" says Donal O'Sheary, says he. "Then here's for my story."

Donal O'Sheary's Story

"When I was a young man of one-and-twenty, my father he was a farmer on the banks of the Foyle, in Derry, and owned as fine and as kindly a farm as any was to be found between here and there—the Farm of the Fort, it was called, by reason that there was a lovely green Fairy Fort rising up sheer out of the holm in the farm's center. My father kept one servant boy and one servant girl, and on a May eve he says to myself, 'Donal,' says he, 'take the boy and the girl with you before break o' day tomorrow, and start off to the bog, and do a good day's footing turf, the three of you.'

"That was well and good. Before break o' day, just as my father directed, myself and the servant boy and girl were out in the gray twilight and facing for the bog. We had to pass by the foot of the Fairy Fort takin' a short cut across the

7

farm, and, behold you! as we were passing it, doesn't Brigid, the girl, clap her hands and cry out, 'Och, see the lovely wee well!' And there, sure enough, was the loveliest little new well ever you rested your eyes on, bubbling up clear, where none of us had ever known before. Says Brigid, says she, stooping down on one knee, 'I'll have a sup out of it for good luck,' and in the palm of her hand she lifted a sup of the water to drink. 'I'll have a sup for good luck, too,' says Rory, says he, stoopin' down for another sup. 'Well,' says I, 'I'll not be behind either, and here goes for a good-luck sup likewise.' We were sthrivin' who'd be quickest to get the first drink. When we drank and stood up, we beheld the strangest happening that ever man beheld before; for Brigid was all at once changed into a brave-lookin' boy, and Rory transformed into a finely dressed, winsome young woman, and I myself changed into a priest! And when we looked around us, we found we were in a strange country entirely!

"Strange and very strange as all this was, curiously enough, it did not seem to be strange to ourselves. I was priest of the parish that I found myself in, and me doing my duties without no

8

wonder in the world either to myself or to any of my congregation; all of whom I knew as if I'd been born and bred among them. The young man and young woman that had been Brigid and Rory, they fell in love with one another without loss of time, and they came to me to marry them; and I married them, and they contentedly began life as parishioners of mine. A model couple they were, more by the same token—and an example to all married couples under me: so that, often and often, when I was preaching on a Sunday, I held the pair up for a parable to my parish. They put in six happy years, and had half a dozen children born to them, that they were rearin' up decently and well—a credit to their parents and the parish. And during the same years I had plenty of work before me, I tell you, to manage a big, unruly parish—and hard I wrought at it. I christened and married hundreds, and buried scores upon scores. I was reforming my parish wonderfully, to the delight of my bishop, who prophesied that there was more than a chance of my filling his seat when he'd be called away. And he was an old man now.

"Well and good. At the end of this time I, one

day, on my way home from a sick call, dropped into the house of the pair that had been Rory and Brigid, to see how they were coming on—as I often used to do. They said I was the very man in all the world they were wishful to see. Next morning being May-day, they were going to take a holiday to themselves, as they had not taken one for six years gone, and they were to drive to the Wood of the Five Oak Trees (a beautiful wood about five miles away), taking lashin's and leavin's of eatin' and drinkin' with them in order to spend a good, healthful, hearty, joyful day: and they wanted myself to join them. I consented.

"So, off we found ourselves driving at daybreak. And, in the very heart of the wood, we built a fire and made our breakfast. When we had made a hearty meal, the eldest boy, who had been running about, came in with the news that he had discovered the most lovely little fountain ever was seen, shooting high in the air and showering lovely spray for far and wide on all sides. We got up and went to view it; and, sure enough, it was a wonderful fountain, and one that, curiously, none of us had ever heard tell of in these woods before. Their eldest little girl had fetched with her a cup, and the water was so clear, and sparkling and beautiful, that she thought she'd like to taste it. She held the cup under the spray till it filled, and she handed round a drink to every one of us. It had the quarest effect you ever knew; for, every one of us got drowsy as soon as we had taken a sup of it, and every one of us stretched out, one here, one there, one yonder, saying we'd have three winks of sleep. We didn't sleep long till we woke up; and when we woke, where do you think we found ourselves but at the bottom of the Fairy Fort on my father's farm! And I wasn't a priest at all, at all, any longer, but only a farmer's son again; and Rory was the young man he had been; and Brigid the same young woman! And, stranger still, no one of us an hour older than we had been on that morning when the first happenin' here happened to us!

"There was never a well to be seen at the foot of the Fairy Fort; neither was there a fountain. And the three of us streeled home to my father, whose eyes stood out in his head to the size of small saucers as he questioned us where we had been since we went from home six years ago that morning? and how it was we all stood still at the same age as when we left? Since we went away, trace nor track of us had never been found, and it was concluded that all three of us had got drowned in a bottomless bog hole. We were prayed for as dead, he told us, and entirely given up for lost.

"I told the story just as it happened, and my father, when he heard it, wouldn't harbor in his house, he said, beings like us, under spells; for we'd bring him ill luck. So he turned us all out, and I for a while worked a day with this man and a day with that, till I earned the price of a pack. I bought that; put it on my back; shook my feet upon the King's highroad, and have been traveling from that day till the storm drove me to your door, Donal O'Donnell, this night.

"There's my story for you. What do you think of it, my good man?"

"I think," says Donal O'Donnell, says he, "that it's the most wonderful thing I ever heard tell of in my life, and it beats out my wonder complete. Sorcha," says he to his wife, "make Donal O'Sheary the best supper the house can afford; and prepare him the best bed."

"And now, boys," says Donal O'Donnell, says

he, to the other two old men, "what do you think of these wonders you have heard? or did any of you ever hear tell of anything to compare with them?"

"Indeed, and I did," says Donal O'Neary, says he.

"You did?" says Donal O'Donell. "Upon my word, if you can tell me anything near as wonderful as either of them, I'll make Sorcha get you a good supper, and a good night's lodging, moreover—which I never did to streeler nor stroller in my life afore."

"Well and good," says Donal O'Neary, taking him at his word. "Then I'l tell you a wonderful happenin' that happened to myself and put me on the road a peddler; and when you've heard it you'll say I've earned a supper and a night's lodging."

"Come, then," says Donal O'Donnell, says he, "come, out with it."

Donal O'Neary's Story

"Well," says Donal O'Neary, says he, "when I was a youth, I was the son of a farmer in the townland of Tawnawilly in Donegal, who was famous for the raising of corn. There was no harvest that he wouldn't put five hundred stacks of corn into his haggard and there was no ware [spring] that he wouldn't put one hundred plough-horses into his fields. There was one particular harvest when he had, as usual, his five hundred stocks of corn stacked in the haggard, and thatched, and roped, and we were all settling ourselves down for a happy winter; when, what would you have of it, we, of a morning, found a stack clean missing and no trace of where it went, or how it had gone. On the next morning, behold ye! another stack was missing; and sight nor sign of a straw of it wasn't to be seen on the countryside. And the morning after that still another was away. It was the most wonderful thing we ever knew of; and the next night I said I'd sit up and watch the haggard; and, of all nights of the year, it was Hallow Eve night. Very good: I put a fine warm coat on me, and I stepped about in the haggard for the first hour or so; and then I crouched under one of the stacks till I would have three winks of sleep; but I was soon wakened out of this by finding the stack, that I lay under, shaking, and hearing a hubbub like a fair. Up I jumped, and, lo and behold ye! the stack itself was covered with little fairy men and women, and the haggard was filled with them, and so was the whole countryside, hill and dale, as far and far as my eye could carry, on that the brightest of moonlight nights. There wasn't a man less than a hundred thousand, and every one pulled a stalk of corn out of this particular stack; and, when he got it, he mounted it, same way as ye see the little children mount a walking-stick, and saying, 'Up, up, my brave brown steed!' each stalk of corn swept off, carrying its rider with it. When they had all taken their stalks, and there was only a bare one left of the whole stack, I lifted it up and mounted it; and I says, as they did, 'Up, up, my brave brown steed,' and away with me!

"At the tail end of the multitude I swept through the air like a streak of lightning, traveling a hundred mile a minute. In very short time the whole host of us struck against the Himalay' Mountains in the Eastern world; and, at a word of command from the leader of us, a door opened in the face of the rocks there, and every one of us rode in, the door closing behind again.

"Such a great and gorgeous place as was within there, it surpasses me to describe to you. There was a dining-hall the length of the holms of Finn-Water, with tables that measured miles; and thousands upon thousands of candles in gold candlesticks, and dishes of all kinds of eatables under the sun, and decanters of all kinds of drink-ables, laid out along these tables. To the feast every one of us sat down, and we ate and drank to our hearts' content; then the tables were cleared away, and, to the music of five thousand pipers and five thousand fiddlers, the dance began. The beautiful fairy queen who had sat at the head of the tables, she came along and asked myself for partner. I objected, saying that, as it was now late in the night, it was time I was setting out for home; else they'd be missing me and not know what had happened.

" 'It's but young in the night yet,' she said, 'and there's a good moon besides. I'll only ask one reel, you and I, just to show these people how to do it. When it's over, we'll give you a horse to go home on that'll not let much grass grow under his hooves.'

"It wasn't an easy matter for me to refuse her,

she was so beautiful and bewitching, and I'm afeared I didn't try to overpower her with objections. Anyhow, we both went out for a reel. All the others who were on the floor cleared off it and ranged themselves round the walls, for to watch the pair of us. A purty fair dancer I always was reckoned to be, although it's myself says it; but I never before made finer dancing than on that night; and, if I was good at it, maybe it's the fairy queen wasn't twice as good; so that the pair of us on the waxed floor was worth coming a hundred miles to see. To the admiration of that multitude and the paralyzing of the pipers and fiddlers, we footed it, the pair of us, hot and fast, for, I'm sure, little less than an hour, finishin' up with a flourish that would do your heart good, took hands and curtshied to all present, and retired to our places amid clapping of hands that was deafening.

"I asked her if it was long after midnight yet; and she said that it was just turned one and that I'd be safe at home in a very few minutes more. She made me promise for to come again the next night before she'd let me go; then she gave me in charge of a little man who led me out to the

17

mountainside again, put a brave brown steed
under me that was worth a hundred pound if a
penny, and told me I was to keep the steed for
coming back again every time I wished; and that,
whenever I chose to come, I might be sure, since
the queen had taken such a fancy to me, there
would be a welcome and twenty before me.

"I thanked him, put spurs to my steed, and
through the air with me at a hundred mile a
minute; and it was hardly five minutes till I
landed plump in my father's haggard; and when
I jumped off my steed, meaning to lead him to the
stables, I found I was holdin' a straw!

"Well, I was in consternation, you may be sure;
but I set off to go into the house. Behold ye!
when I came to the house it wasn't my father's
long, low, thatched house was it, at all, at all, but
a great big three-story-high house with a grand
carriage drive up to the door. There was a big
bulldog chained close by, who made a dash at me,
and, only his chain wasn't long enough, would
have torn me to pieces. When he couldn't get at
me, he began for to howl fit to waken the dead.
A window was thrown up on the second story,
and a man with a nightcap on his head and a gun

in his hand, leaned out, and he yelled for whatever robber was there to get away or he'd blow his brains out.

"I went away as fast as I could; and me, as you may well suppose, lost in wonderment and feeling deranged in the head. I wandered about the country till morning; but, though I knew every field and every road and every hill and every stream, there wasn't a house in it that I knew at all, at all. Some of them were great houses built in the stead of the nice little thatch ones that I knew. Other houses I come to that had been great yesterday, and found them nothing but a few old stones on top of one another, and nettles growing over them! Then I surely felt there must be something the matter with me; but I waited till morning, and till people got about and were going to the fields. Not a face of all the faces I met did I know. I mustered enough courage, at last, to ask if this was the land of Tawnawilly I was in, and the parties I asked looked me up and down, strange, and said, 'Yes, stranger, it is. Where do you come from?'

" 'Stranger!' says I. 'Do you not know me—

young Donal O'Neary, son of old Donal O'Neary, the warmest farmer in Tawnawilly?'

"They looked at me quare, and passed on, and I seen them shaking their heads and whispering to one another when I looked. Then I surely believed that my head had been touched. But I went into a very, very old kind of a cabin that, it seemed to me, I should know the looks of; and there I found a very, very old man on one side of the fire, and a very, very old woman on the other side, nodding across the hearth at one another, and they not less than ninety years of age, if they were a day. I asked them if either of them knew where I could find Donal O'Neary of Tawnawilly; and, when I said that, both of them looked up at me strange, and the old woman shook her head and said there wasn't now, nor never was, one of that name in the townland. But the old man, he said to me, 'Hold on, ye!' and he begun for to think; and he said, 'Yes, indeed, there *was* one of the name in this townland.' He turned to the old woman and says he, 'My poor old father (God rest him! he'll be dead fourscore years again' Candlemas) used to tell me, when I was a youngster, a quare story about one Donal O'Neary, who died

20

fifty years before my father was born, and who
had a son Donal, a fine, strapping young man, they
said, who went out of a Hallow Eve night to
watch the corn-stacks that were a-stealing from
his father's haggard, and teetotally disappeared—
to what art or part nobody ever knew—and no
sign of him was ever seen more. The old man
lived twenty years longer, a broken-hearted creature over the loss of such a brave son, and then
went to a welcome grave. . . . Sure it isn't a
legacy,' said he to me, 'you're going to look for
from a man who is in his grave these two hundred
years?'

"As the old fellow was telling me this story,
I happened to see, fornenst me, the wizened visage
of another very old man. And, behold ye! wasn't
it a looking-glass I was gazing into. It was my
own face—a withered old man I found myself
instead, of the bright young fellow I thought to
be, in it.

"To make a long story short, the people in
Tawnawilly came to the conclusion that I was
a demented man, and they pitied me so much that
I had to go from among them. I begged the price
of a pack; for, old as I was, I wanted to earn my

own living. I put it on my back and went out into the world.

"That," says he, "was a year ago; and I have been traveling and peddling since; till the storm drove me to your door tonight. And there's my story for ye."

"Well, well, well, well!" says Donal O'Donnell, says he. "I thought Donal O'Sheary's story was wonderful, but that one is ten times more wonderful still! Sorcha, will you get this poor old man the best supper the house can afford, and the softest bed? . . . For you have earned it," says Donal O'Donnell, says he, to Donal O'Neary.

"Thank you," says Donal O'Neary.

"I'm sorry," says Donal O'Donnell, says he, then, turning to Donal O'Leary, "to be making any distinctions; but I'm afeared, my good man, you'll have to go to travelin', as I don't suffer neither streelers nor strollers to remain over in my house, without very special reason."

"But if I could show you very special reason?" says Donal O'Leary, says he.

"How?" says Donal O'Donnell.

"Tell as wonderful a happening that happened

22

to me as any that happened to either of my name-
sakes."

"Well, if you done that," says Donal O'Donnell,
"you'd have the best supper and the best bed my
house could give—and be well desarvin' of them,
too," says he.

"Well and good," says Donal O'Leary. "Then
hear to my tale:

Donal O'Leary's Story

"When I was a young man," says he, "I was
son of a farmer who owned a fine farm that ran
by the white strand of Teelin. There was a beautiful day in harvest, and my father had a *methial*
of men shearing corn. I was joined with the men
myself, cutting away from early morning; and,
tor'st twelve o'clock in the day, my father said to
me, 'Donal,' says he, 'it's drawing on time your
mother would be making the men's dinner. Go
home,' says he, 'and carry her in some water from
the well on the strand.'

"I threw down my hook, and I went home;
and my mother gave me a pair of water-buckets,
and I went down, singing, to the well on the strand

23

to draw a *go* of water. The water in the well,
when I got to it, was so clear and so beautiful and
so very enticing that, leaving the buckets out of
my hands by the well-side, I went upon my knees
and stooped to take a sup of it. But, as I went to
drink, doesn't I see down in the well the reflection of the shore, and of the beautiful full tide that
washed Teelin's white strand—and, coming sailing along the beautiful tide, a lovely little boat in
full sail, that, faster than you could say it, sailed
right into the strand below me. I jumped up, and
there, sure enough, was the little boat just grating
on the gravel. Down I ran to it, and began ad-
mirin' it, and then I stepped in to see what it was
like inside; and the minute I got in, off sails the
boat from the strand, and away with it from the
shore—away to the west'ard, carrying myself
along.

"It was the smoothest and beautifulest sail ever
I had; and so enchanting was it that I never felt
one bit alarmed, though I seen Teelin's strand
leave my sight, and Teelin's hills; and then the
great mountain of Sliabh Liag, all sink away. For
three days and three nights I went straight west,
never knowing hunger nor thirst, but every hour

pleasanter and lovelier than the other. On the evening of the third day a delightful green land rose over the water, and in short time we ran in on a dazzling white strand.

"A gorgeous castle with thirteen towers to it rose on a green *knowe* above the strand. I stepped from the boat, and marched up to the castle. The hall door was wide open and I walked in, and I found myself in a great and grand hall, where there were hundreds of the beautifulest damsels eye ever beheld; some of them combing their hair, and other of them embroidering on silks and satins; some of them reclining on couches; more of them in groups chatting; and still others singing and dancing to the most entrancing music ever was heard. But there was one damsel far beautifuler, and far, far grander than all the rest, sitting upon a golden throne at the head of the hall, with thirteen of the rarest of maidens to each side of her.

"When I come into the hall, she beckoned for me to approach her, and she set me on a silver throne beside her own golden one, and welcomed me to the Island of Fair Women. She begun for to discourse me in the sweetest tones and with the sweetest discourse ever heard on earth afore;

and I didn't know one minute from another minute, or one hour from another hour, as I sat there, all enchanted, harkening to her. I could have listened for a hundred years as easy as an hour, and been as greedy for more at the end as I was at the beginning.

"However, she said that she and her three hundred fair damsels had long been waiting and wishing for me; and that it was she who had sent her magic boat to Ireland and to Teelin's white strand on the morning that she found me going to the well for water, knowing it would bring me back to her.

"At night, I was given a gorgeous room in that most gorgeous castle, and a bed where you'd sink so far in the soft down that you'd hardly know your way back to earth again in the morning.

"In the morning I was sitting beside the Queen of the Island of Fair Women again, she on her gold throne and me on my silver one, and hundreds of fair women through the hall, dancing and singing, and enjoying themselves in all manners of ways; and if I enjoyed myself well the first day, my pleasant discoursing with the Queen was double as enjoyable this day.

26

"For three weeks this went on, I wooing every day; and at the end of the three weeks we were married. And a wedding beautifuler or grander than what we had was never before known in the world: the festivities and rejoicings lasted nine days and nine nights, and the last day and night were better than the first.

"Well and good. To make a long story short, the beauty of that island was past all I'd eve dreamt of, and my days were all happier one than another with me. Beautiful birds of all the colors of the rainbow, and of the sweetest tones that men ever conceived, made music, day and night, in the woods. The trees drooped with heavy loads of the rarest of fruits and of flowers; and the flowers on the ground were as thick as the heather on the mountain without. Every day that island was brighter and more beautiful than the day gone afore, and every hour was happier than the other hour. I knew neither worry nor care, and my mind was as carefree and gay as the gayest of the song-birds that sang in the trees.

"Months went past so; and years passed so; and scores of years passed so. And a family of thirteen fair children grew up round us, and were

27

married, and had children again, that were, if
such could be, fairer than themselves. The quarest thing was that, though many were born, no
one ever died—all grew up to be beautiful young
men and women; and halted there; for no soul
in the island showed older than twenty-five; and
youth was both on their cheeks and in their hearts.

"When I had lived a hundred years on this
island, it was only like ten, so happy had I been.
And when I had lived two hundred years, it was
like twenty; and when I had lived three hundred
years, I thought it hardly thirty, so full of ioy
and free from care was it.

"At the end of three hundred years, however,
I one day took a longing and felt a loneliness to
see Ireland and Teelin's white strand once more.
I told this to my fair bride, and she objected. But
the loneliness and the longing grew and grew on
me, and I beseeched her and beseeched, till, at long
and at last, she had to give in to me for peace' sake,
and allow me to go and satisfy myself with one
good look at it. She had her magic boat prepared,
and the sails set, and, after she had embraced and
kissed me, she handed me into it, with many

weighty warnings. The boat was to sail along the
edge of Teelin's white strand, and give me a fair
and full view of all. But, on peril of my happiness, I was on no account to step from the boat,
or let foot of me touch earth. I gave faithful
promise to observe all this. I kissed her good-by,
and off the boat started, sailing fast and far. I
sailed for three pleasant days and three pleasant
nights, and, on a morning bright and beautiful, the
boat bore in upon Teelin's fair strand, and coasted
along it. It came opposite to our own little well
upon the strand, and when I seen this beautiful
little well I was filled with a great longing for to
take a drink from it—a longing that I couldn't
resist. I remembered my promise: but then, I
said, I'd only just be one bare minute out, and no
one would be the wiser. I'd run to the well, take
three sups, and back again, satisfied, and happy
at heart, and ready for another three hundred un-
fretting years in the Island of Fair Women.

"I threw out the anchor, jumped upon the
strand, and away to the well with me. I went
down on my knees to take my three sups; but behold ye! as I did, what did I see shining in the

well below but the shadow of two wooden buckets that I used to fetch to the well before I left Teelin long ago; and, likewise, I sees the reflection of the tide, and, O Heaven save me! the little boat I had anchored sailing away out over it.

"I lifted up my head; and there, sure enough, by the well-side, were the two old wooden buckets, just in the very selfsame spot I had left them down when I stooped to drink here three hundred years before: and when I looked behind me to the shore, there was my beautiful little boat sailing away, off and off, fast and fast, and disappearing completely to the west'ard!

"I stood there for a good while in quandary, till, at last, I heard a voice calling loud and sharp to me, 'Donal, are you going to stay away all day with the *go* of water?' It was my mother's voice; and a mystified man was I. I took hold of the buckets in a sort of half-dream, and dipping them into the well, got the full of them, and traveled up, and walked into our own house. And when I came in, my mother scolded me, saying, 'It's a shame for you, Donal, for taking ten minutes to fetch a *go* of water from a well that isn't fifty yards from the house hardly. The poor men'll be late with their dinner!'

"When I came to myself properly, I tried to persuade them into what happened me; and they thought me gone in my mind. And the more I tried to argue the thing, the worse they believed me to be. At length, the very little children nick-named me 'The Wanderin' Man,' and things got so uncomfortable that, before a week passed, I had to beg my father for the price of a peddler's pack. I bought it, and mounted it on my back, and faced the world with it.

"And peddling I've been ever since, till the storm drove me to your door the night. And that's my story."

"Well, well, well, well!" says Donal O'Donnell, says he. "I thought what happened to myself was wonderful: I thought what happened to Donal O'Sheary more wonderful; and what happened to Donal O'Neary more wonderful still. But the happening that happened to you is the wonder-fulest happening, surely, that ever I in my life-time heard tell of; and you've earned a supper for a lord and a bed for a king. . . . Sorcha," says he, "pull down the table and put on plates for four and suppers for fourteen—the best the house can afford. . . . As long as I live," says he to Donal O'Sheary, Donal O'Neary, and Donal O'Leary, "I'll never again turn from my door a streeler or a stroller."

And, on behalf of all streelers and strollers, they thanked him right heartily.

The night was wilder and wilder without—one of the wildest nights that ever blew in the wild Gap of Barnesmor; but they didn't mind it one bit; they had made up their minds to make a night of it. And they divided the night into three parts. The first part of it they gave to eating and drinking to satisfaction; the second part of it they gave to story-telling and poem-reciting; and the third part of it they gave to sleep. And a more enjoyable night, Donal O'Donnell gave in, he had never enjoyed in all his born days afore.

When morning came, they had all breakfasted heartily and well, they shook hands with and thanked Donal O'Donnell and his good woman Sorcha, and they mounted their packs, and set foot upon the road again—every man facing his own path; and left Donal O'Donnell pining and longing for more streelers and strollers to come soon to his door again seeking for shelter that they'd surely find.

And that's the story of The Wonders of the Three Donals.

THE SWORD OF LIGHT

ONCE upon a time, long, long ago, there was a Prince of Donegal, who died and left all his castles, and all his cattle, and all his wealth in gold and silver and jewels, to his son Niall, who had always been such a great spendthrift that his father knew well he would soon run through the fortune, even if it had been ten times as great; and, knowing this, the father on his deathbed said to him:

"Niall," says he, "when you have drunk and spent my castle and my cattle and my wealth, and you have nothing else for it, go and hang yourself," says he, "on a certain branch of a certain tree"—mentioning it—"in the garden."

Niall promised this to his father, and then his father died; and right enough, the father wasn't cold in the grave till Niall was making the wealth and money spin, and a gay old time of it he had, no doubt, while his fortune lasted. But at the rate he went it could not last always if he owned the wealth of the East; and to the end of his money he came.

And then despair came on the poor fellow, and he saw that his father's advice was a wise one. So to the certain branch of the certain tree that his father had told him of, Niall went, tied a rope to the branch, put a noose on the end of it, and kicked himself off. But, lo and behold you! the moment his weight came on the branch, down broke the branch, and out from the hole in the tree, at the spot where the branch tore away from it, rolled piles of money. And it was then and again that my glad Niall blessed his father ten times over for having hidden away this store for him, and put him upon such a grand way of finding it.

But though his poor father may have thought otherwise, Niall's loss was no lesson to him. He soon made this money, too, spin by drinking and carousing and gambling; for a greater gambler than Niall wasn't to be found again between the four winds of the world; and the black day came at length when he hadn't two gold pieces to rap against one another. If things had been black for Niall before, they looked far blacker now.

Well, one night at this time, Niall was going home from the gambling house where he had spent his very last penny, and he swithering in his own mind what he was going to do, at all, at all, or whether there was any use in living any longer; and as he leaped over a ditch, what does he nearly leap on top of only a Big Red Fellow, who was playing cards, his right hand against his left, and he arguing fast and furious for the one hand or the other.

"Well, well, well!" says Niall, says he. "That's the drollest thing ever I have seen. What foolishness are ye at, at all, at all?"

"Come, come," says the Big Fellow, says he, "sit down and have a game of cards with me. I'm ill off for some one to beat, for I haven't got one to play me a game this seven years; and all that time I have been playing the way ye see me, my right hand against my left; and it's no ways fair anyhow, for my left hand's so cunning that it's ever and always winning."

"There isn't any use," says Niall, says he, "in my sitting down, for I haven't a penny between me and poverty."

"That's the reason why it is of use for ye to sit down," says the Red Fellow, "for ye may win a fortune off me."

"And what will I stake?" says Niall.

"Oh!" says the other, "ye'll not be at a loss for a stake. Sure, ye can stake your services to me for a year and a day if I win, and if I lose ye'll have any wish your heart grieves for."

"Good, good!" says Niall, says he. "That's both fair and square, and I'm willing."

And down he sits, and to the game the two of them falls, and it wasn't long till the game was decided, and my brave Niall had won.

"Well, what's your pleasure?" says the Red Fellow, says he.

"It is," says Niall, "that my father's castle and court should be mended and built from the deplorable state it has fallen into; that there should be servants in the hall, coaches in the yard, and steeds in their stalls."

"Go home," says the Red Fellow. "You have your wish."

And true enough, when my brave Niall reached home, there, to his great rejoicement, he finds his father's castle and court better and finer and grander than ever it had been in the memory of man. There were richly dressed servants in the hall, gold coaches in the yard, and all the stables crammed to the door with steeds the finest that ever were ridden or driven, and Niall was a proud and happy man.

So lucky had he been on that night, that again, about midnight of the next night, he couldn't resist going to the hill where he met the Red Fellow, to see if he would have the good fortune to fall in with him again; and the good fortune he had, right enough. There he met with the Red Fellow, he seated in the selfsame spot, playing his right hand against his left, just like the night before, and he cheating and scolding over the one hand or the other, for all he was worth.

"I'm glad to see ye, Niall," says he. "Will ye sit down till we have a hand at the cards this night again?"

Now, it was little coaxing Niall wanted. Down he sat, staking a year's services against the granting of a wish, and, as good luck would have it, Niall won again.

"What's your wish?" says the Red Fellow.

"It is," says Niall, "that all my father's hills and glens should be stocked again with the cattle and sheep that I drunk and spent."

"Ye have your wish," says the Red Fellow, says he, "and go home."

Home Niall went, rejoicing in his heart; for all the way over the hills and the glens the music in his ears was the lowing of cattle and the bleating of sheep; and when he looked out from his castle window early the next morning, and viewed the hills and the dales alive with fine animals, it was pleasant for Niall's eyes, I tell you.

Well, to make a long story short, Niall wasn't yet content; so that night again found him on the hill and playing cards with the Red Fellow once more for the selfsame stakes. That night again Niall won; and the wish Niall asked was to have for his wife the beautifullest woman in the world, either above ground or below it.

This wish didn't more than half please the Red Fellow.

"Oh!" says he, "as you won it, you will have your wish, though that woman I intended for my-self."

39

And when Niall got home, the beautifullest woman in the world—for surely she was the beautifullest—was there before him, for wife. And now he surely would be happy.

His wife said to him next night: "This time again you may go to meet the Red Fellow, for I see you want to do it; but take one word of advice from me. If you win, as I believe you will, let your wish be this, and only this: to have the pick of all the horses in his stables; and no matter how many or how grand are the horses he shows you, you are to choose none but the worst-looking wee, shaggy, brown nag that he has, and the worst-looking saddle and bridle upon it."

Niall promised her request; and when he met the Red Fellow that night, and they played and he won, and the Red Fellow asked him what was his wish, Niall said:

"My wish is the pick of all the horses in your stables."

The Red Fellow he looked glum for a minute; but then he says, "You will have your wish." So he put to his mouth a whistle, and he blew it, and that instant Niall found himself standing with the Red Fellow in a stable that had three hundred stalls, and a great, beautiful, shining black horse in every stall.

"There's the best horses in my stable," says the Red Fellow. "Which of them will ye have?"

"I'll have none of them," says Niall.

Then the Red Fellow looked glum again, but he blew on his whistle, and that instant they were both of them standing in another stable in which were three hundred stalls, with a beautiful chestnut horse in very stall—the finest and grandest animals that Niall had ever seen.

"Well, there's my second best stable," says the Red Fellow. "Which of them will ye have?"

"There's none of them pleasin' to me, I thank you," says Niall. "Show me another stable."

So the Red Fellow blew the whistle a third time, and they were in a stable in which were three hundred stalls, with beautiful horses, every one as white as the driven snow, standing in each stall.

"There," says the Red Fellow, "that's my third best stable. Which horse will ye have?"

"I will have none of them," says Niall. "There's none of them pleasin' to me."

The Red Fellow was mad with anger now, and says he, "I have no other stable—only a stable of wee old nags, one of which wouldn't be worth taking with you."

"No matter," says Niall, says he. "Let me see it."

The Red Fellow was in a towering rage; but he blew his whistle, and they were standing in the stable of nags. Niall walked down the row of nags till he came to the very last and worst one in it.

"This one," says Niall, says he, "is the one I will take; and that," says he, pointing to the worst and tornest and ugliest saddle and bridle hanging on the walls—"that," says he, "is the saddle and bridle I want."

The Red Fellow was black in the face with wrath, and says he: "I will not give you that wretched old nag or that torn old saddle or bridle, for they're one and all a disgrace; and I'll not let the likes of them be seen going out of my stables."

"Come, come, come," says Niall, says he. "I don't want any nonsense; be they bad or be they good, it's my wish to have them, and, since I won the game, my wish is my command."

So, raging though the fellow was, he had to let

Niall saddle and bridle the old nag; and then Niall got on the nag's back; and three leaps of the nag landed him at his own door.

His lovely wife she was glad to see him back. "And now," she says, "my poor Niall, you have got all in the world you want, and on the peril of your life, and as I love you, never more go to meet the Red Fellow or to play a game of cards, for if you do you will surely rue it, and I warn you."

Niall promised his wife that he wouldn't go next or near him again or have anything more to do with him. And he meant to keep his promise. He did keep it for three days; but on the third night after, the old gambling instinct overcame poor Niall, and he sneaked off unknownst to his wife, and away to the hill again. And, sure enough, in the selfsame spot the Red Fellow was there, playing his right hand against his left, and arguing and cheating and scolding and brow-beating the one hand against the other.

"You're welcome, Niall," says he; "and will ye sit down and have a game of cards?"

"That's what I come for," says Niall. So down the both of them sits, and plays upon the old terms.

And, lo and behold you! my poor Niall lost. The Red Fellow, when he found this, laughed long and loud.

"For a year and a day now, my boy, you're in my power," says he, "to send you on any service I like. I have got good service for you; and if you don't perform it you will lose your head."

"Let me hear," says poor Niall, says he, "what the service is, anyhow."

"Hear it ye will," says the Red Fellow, "though do it I am afeard ye never will. It is," says he, "two things: to find for me who killed the Knight of Glandore; and to fetch me the Sword of Light that is owned by the King of the Eastern World —and that within a year and a day, or else lose your head."

Full sadly and sorrowfully poor Niall he went home, and the wife saw him in such low spirits next day that she knew well there was something wrong, and she worried him up and down to tell her what it was; and Niall at length told her.

"My poor Niall," says she, "you wouldn't be warned by me. It's bad, and bad, and bad enough; but God is good," says she, "and there's no knowing what good fortune is in store for us. So we will take it as lightly as we can, and hope for the best."

Niall he was for setting off at once on the search, but she wouldn't let him. She said, "If it can be got in twelve months, it can surely be got in nine, so you will spend three months with me, for maybe I will never see you more."

Niall he agreed; and when the three months were spent the wife said, "If the Sword of Light can be got in nine months, it can be surely got in six; so you will spend three more months with me." And Niall he spent three more.

Then she said, "If the Sword of Light can be got in six months, it can surely be got in three; and so you will spend three more months with me." And another three months Niall did spend.

Then there was nine months of it gone, and both of them agreed that though it was sad and sad, they'd have to part. She told Niall that the King of the Eastern World was brother to her own father, and if any one could help him her father could and would. She told him that Gillie Rua of the Hill, the man with whom he had been playing cards, was a bad man who had always hated her

45

father and her uncle; he had stolen her from her father's mountain to make her his wife; and he had stolen her father's Steed of Swiftness, which was the nag that Niall now owned. He was a man of many powers, and the only thing that kept him under was the fact that the King of the Eastern World owned the Sword of Light, which held him in mortal terror. If he had that Sword, she said, he meant to rule and ruin the world.

She mounted Niall upon the nag, and before she parted with him gave him her ring. She told him to ride to her father's castle in the Indies, and when he showed that ring as a token, her father would assist him all was in his power. Then Niall kissed her and set off.

At every bound the steed gave he cleared seven hills, seven rills, and seven glens; he could catch the swift wind before, and the swift wind behind could not catch him. And after a long and long journey, over hills and leas, lands and seas, Niall reached the castle of the King of the Indies, who was his wife's father.

The King knew his own steed. He welcomed Niall, who didn't yet tell he had married his

46

daughter, and spread a feast in his honor. At
the feast, when Niall was filling out a glass of wine
for the Queen, he dropped his wife's ring in it,
and when she drank the wine and found the ring,
she and the King knew it, and asked Niall how he
had come by it; and Niall told them. Then there
was wonder and rejoicing, for when the Gillie Rua
had carried their daughter away they thought she
was lost to them forever.

Nothing now was too good for Niall, and he was
treated like a Prince. Next day he told the King
of the Indies the journey on which he had come,
and asked his advice and assistance.

He told Niall that he had come on a perilous
enterprise. The Gillie Rua, he said, had won each
game and sent three thousand heroes on that enterprise before, and no one of them ever returned
alive; but he prayed and hoped it would be better
with poor Niall. He said, "I will give you the
best advice I can, anyhow, and do all that's in my
power to get you the information and the Sword.
The King of the Eastern World," he says, "lives
from here a long day's journey on your nag. He
has three walls round his castle, and every wall is
three miles high, and every gate defies the power

47

of man to get through. In his castle there are
twelve rooms, one within the other, a door to every
room, an armed guard upon every door. In the
twelfth room the King keeps the Sword of Light,
and there he sleeps himself; it is he, too, who knows
the secret of who killed the Knight of Glandore.
What you will do," says he to Niall, "is to start off
tomorrow and ride to his castle. When you get
there leap the outside wall, rattle loud on the second gate, and cry out your demand for the Sword
of Light to be given you. Lose no time," says he,
"but at that instant put your horse at the wall again,
clear it and come home before the wind. I will
have all my gates lying open for you to dash in. If
you make one instant's delay anywhere, you are a
dead man."

Niall promised he would do all this; and the
next morning, sure enough, he started out upon his
nag. It took seven rills, seven hills, and seven
glens at every leap; it caught the wind before, and
the wind behind could not catch it. He reached
the castle of the King of the Eastern World, and,
putting his nag at the outside wall, which was
three miles high, cleared it. He rattled on the
second gate and shouted as loud as he could shout,

"I command the King of the Eastern World to tell me the secret, who killed the Knight of Glandore, and to deliver to me the Sword of Light."

That instant the three gates and the twelve doors of the castle flew open, and the King of the Eastern World was standing on the doorstep with a look of thunder on his face.

Niall he didn't wait one moment, but, putting the nag at the wall again, cleared it and went home before the wind. The King of the Eastern World was at his heels with the Sword of Light, which dazzled half the earth whenever it was unsheathed, in his hand; and as Niall dashed in through the gates a third of his nag's tail was cut off, but the gates were closed the next instant, and he was safe. The King and the Queen congratulated poor Niall, and said he had done well.

"On the morrow," says the King, "you will have to repeat the very same performance—only this," says he, "that you will find the outside wall now fallen; and if you are as successful tomorrow, the second wall will fall also. On the third day you will have to do the selfsame thing, and then the third wall will fall."

49

Well, to make a long story short, on the morrow Niall set out and went through the selfsame performance, and had the selfsame terrible chase after him; and as he and his nag got in through the gates of the friendly King a second third was cut off his nag's tail by the Sword of the King of the Eastern World. But he was successful, and the second wall fell. On the third day he went through the same performance again, and he escaped, too, with the loss of the remaining third of the nag's tail.

The King of the Indies congratulated Niall, and said that he was more than fortunate. "When you have done so well so far," says he, "I think you might manage to win through. I'll give you help and directions for the morrow, which will be the final trial."

So on the next day the King gave Niall a magical Harp of Harps which he owned, and Niall slung it over one shoulder, and the King gave him a bag of withered beech-leaves which he slung over the other shoulder. And after the King had given him instructions he set off upon his nag.

When he reached the castle of the King of the Eastern World he began to play upon his harp;

and when they heard the enchanting music all the servants and all the guards and all the soldiers left every door and thronged out and stood around him, listening in wonder and enchantment; and after a while Niall threw among them his bagful of withered beech-leaves, and their senses were so enchanted that they scrambled and fought for the withered leaves, thinking they were gold and jewels. Niall walked into the castle through the twelve doors, playing on his harp as he went.

The King, who lay in the twelfth room, was enchanted by the music, too, and fell into a deep, sweet, sleep; and when Niall reached the room he saw the Sword of Light hung in its scabbard above the King's head. As the King of the Indies had warned him that when any man tried to draw the Sword from its scabbard it always gave three leaps that shook, and three roars that startled, half the world, Niall set his teeth and caught the Sword by the hilt and pulled with all his might. It gave the first leap and the first roar; the teeth in Niall's head shook, and he thought his ears would never hear again. The King of the Eastern World rolled over in his sleep.

At the second pull the Sword of Light gave another leap and another roar greater and louder than the first and the King rolled over once more, but went to sleep again.

Niall gathered all his nerve and all his strength and gave the third and last pull, and pulled it out of its sheath. It gave a third leap and roar more terrifying far than the other two together, and the third roar aroused the King; but Niall waved the Sword over his head and threatened to have his life if he wouldn't tell him the secret of who killed the Knight of Glandore. The King saw he was at Niall's mercy, and told him, what had never been told to mortal man before, the secret that he himself had killed him.

When the King of the Eastern World heard that Gillie Rua of the Hill was now to get the Sword of Light, he was in great despair, for he said, "There is now no power in all the world to check him; he will murder and slay all before him."

"Never mind," said Niall; "keep up your heart. Little as you love him, maybe I love him less, and may yet get even with him."

Niall returned to his father-in-law's with the Sword of Light and the secret; and great was the rejoicing there when he came. His father-in-law, too, said that if Gillie Rua got the Sword of Light there would never be peace or comfort in the world more. Said he to Niall, "You are under *geasa* to fetch him the Sword and the secret. Bring them to him. When he has got the Sword of Light, he will flourish it and say that he has now the power of the world and the most perfect sword in it. Say you in reply that it would be the most perfect only for one fault. He will ask you what is that fault. You will reach your hand for the Sword to point out the fault, and when you get it in your hand again, sweep the head off him."

Niall was rejoiced at these directions. He set out upon his nag, for it was now the last day of his service. The nag took seven rills, seven hills, and seven glens at every leap; it could catch the wind before and the wind behind could not catch it; and at length he reached the hill of Gillie Rua and met him there.

"It's welcome you are, Niall," says Gillie Rua. "You have got the Sword, and have you got the secret?"

"There's the Sword," says Niall, handing it to

him, "and the secret is that it was the King of the Eastern World who killed the Knight of Glandore."

"Hurrah!" says Gillie Rua of the Hill. "I'll soon revenge it; for I have now the power of the world and the most perfect sword in it."

"The most perfect it would be but for one fault," says Niall.

"What's that?" says Gillie Rua.

Niall reached his hand for the Sword, and the other gave it to him; and the minute Niall got it he cut off Gillie Rua's head with one sweep.

Little time he lost, then, riding home to his wife, who was the rejoiced woman to see him, and the happy one, I tell you. When he had spent long enough with her, feasting and rejoicing, he set out and brought again to the King of the Eastern World the Sword of Light and made him happy. His wife's father, the King of the Indies, bestowed upon him the Steed of Swiftness, and gave him half his kingdom as a fortune with his wife; and Niall was crowned King and she was crowned Queen, and there was feasting for a year and a day. There were three hundred fiddlers and three hundred pipers who never ceased playing for all that time. I was there and enjoyed myself, and so would you if you had been at it, too.

And it's sorrow for you not being there is the only sorrow I've known then, or since.

CALLY COO-COO O' THE WOODS

ONCE upon a time there were a King and a Queen of Donegal who had three handsome daughters. They had also a Wishing-Chair, which every time you sat in, it could get you anything you wished for. But they kept the Wishing-Chair locked in a room where the daughters never got at it.

It came round that the King of Ulster once gave a great feast, to which the King and Queen of Donegal went. And while they were gone, the daughters, having all the keys, said it would be great fun to go and see the Wishing-Chair.

And when they opened the Wishing-Chair room, and beheld the Wishing-Chair, they said it would be great fun to sit and wish in it.

No sooner said than done. Down in the Chair sat the eldest daughter, and wished she had the richest man in the world. Down after her sat the second daughter, and wished she had the handsomest man in the world. And then sat down the third and youngest, Maeve—who was fond of going into the woods and calling "Cally Coo-Coo!" between her hands to hear the Echo from far away answer, "Cally Coo-Coo!"—down sat Maeve and wished that she had Cally Coo-Coo o' the Woods.

All at once the handsomest man in the world was with them, and the richest man in the world, and Cally Coo-Coo o' the Woods, who came in the shape of a bull, and they were all married within the hour, and each Princess went off with her husband.

Cally Coo-Coo took Maeve away into the depths of the woods, where, under a waterfall, he made a house for her from branches of trees.

Then he disclosed to her that he who had always answered her when she called, and whom people thought was the Echo, was really a Prince of the East; that he had been enchanted by a witch long ago, but the time of his enchantment was now nearly over. He was condemned to be a bull half the time, and a man the other half—a man by night and a bull by day.

After a year a young son was born to them.

Cally Coo-Coo had told her that as soon as the child was born, it would be carried off; and had warned her on the peril of her life not to lose a tear over it.

And sure enough as soon as the child was born it disappeared. And sorry, sorry was Maeve; but, remembering Cally Coo-Coo's warning, she did not drop one tear.

At the end of the second year, a little girl was born. Cally Coo-Coo likewise warned her this time, but she was now so sorely grieved that she lost control of herself, and dropped one tear. However, she caught this tear in her handkerchief, and rolled it up and laid it in her breast.

Cally Coo-Coo's time of enchantment was now near ending, and Maeve's father and mother, the King and Queen of Donegal, invited herself and her sisters, with their husbands, to come to a great Feast of Forgiveness, as the Queen pined to see her daughters again, and to know their husbands.

On the day that was appointed, they all arrived at their father's castle—Cally Coo-Coo coming in the shape of a bull, with Maeve. Her two sisters, and her two sister's husbands, made sport of the husband that Maeve had, and her mother was greatly grieved over it.

At night Cally Coo-Coo, of course, always cast his hide and took the shape of a man. After they had all retired, the Queen wanted to look on her daughters and their husbands in their sleep. When she came to Maeve's room she saw the bull's hide and horns lying on the floor, and Cally Coo-Coo, asleep in bed, the handsomest young man she had ever beheld.

"What a pity," she said, "that such a handsome young man should wear that nasty bull's hide!" So she gathered it with her, and put it into the big hall fire to burn up.

The moment the hide began burning, Cally Coo-Coo, with a frightful scream, jumped up in his bed.

All came flocking to his room, inquiring what was the matter.

He asked who had put his bull's hide into the fire.

The Queen said she had done it; because as he was such a beautiful young man, it was a pity for him to wear that ugly thing.

Then said he, "You have ruined me! I have been under enchantment, and in three days more the spell would have ended, and I would have been a free man, and happy with my Maeve, here, all my life. But now I must undergo worse witchery still, and fly to my own country again."

At that instant into a black crow he was turned, and flew out of the window.

Up jumped Maeve, and away after, piteously crying and calling on him to wait. Wait or pause the crow could not, but flew on and on, while on and on Maeve followed, keeping as close as she could behind him. When he was on the hilltop she was in the hollow, and when she had reached the hilltop, he was in the hollow.

In that way she followed him all the night and all the next day, and when the next night fell, he perched for the first time on a tree, and she came and threw herself down beneath it.

Cally Coo-Coo said: "Get up and go forward, Maeve, and you'll meet a house where you will stop for the night."

She got up and went forward, and did not travel far till she saw a light, and found a little house,

which she entered. There was one woman in the house, and also a little boy who played *caman**
on the floor with a silver caman and a golden nag. All at once Maeve was struck by his resemblance to Cally Coo-Coo.

She asked to be allowed to stop for the night.

The woman welcomed her, gave her a good supper, and a soft bed; and a deep, tired sleep she slept.

She told the woman her story before she left the house in the morning, and the woman said she would like to make her a present which would yet be useful to her. She gave Maeve a needle, one stitch with which would turn any rag of cloth into most beautiful silk, sparkling with showers of silver and gold. She said, "It is the Needle of Beauty. It will prove of great use to you."

Maeve took the Needle of Beauty, thanked the woman very heartily, kissed the child who was so like Cally Coo-Coo,—and set out.

Finding the crow ready to set off, she followed it faithfully this day again. When the crow was on the hilltop, Maeve was in the hollow, and

---

*An ancient Irish game (still played by all Irish boys). Hockey is a modern, devitalized form of it.

when Maeve had reached the hilltop, the crow was in the hollow.

At night he perched in a tree, and she came and lay down beneath it.

He told her to go on until she reached a house where she would stop for the night.

She did not go far till she saw a light, and drew near it, and found a little house.

Going in, she found one woman there, and a very little baby girl, who was amusing herself rolling a golden clue off a silver reel. Maeve was instantly struck with the wonderful resemblance of this child to herself. The child, however, had lost one eye.

The woman of the house welcomed her, and gave her a hearty supper, and a soft bed, where she slept a deep, tired sleep.

In the morning she told the woman her story. And before she left, the woman presented her with a towel, one rub of which over any woman's face, no matter how ugly she had been, would immediately make of her a most beautiful damsel. She said, "It is the Towel of Loveliness. It will yet be useful to you."

Maeve took the towel and thanked her.

Said the woman: "I have one request to make of you."

"What is that?" asked Maeve.

"Give me that which lies next your heart."

Maeve took from her breast the handkerchief in which was rolled the tear she let drop at the loss of her baby-girl, and gave it to the woman.

The woman shook this on the little child's head, and instantly it got its lost eye again.

Maeve thanked the woman, and kissed the child, and set out to follow the crow again. And when she was in the hollow the crow was on the hilltop, and when she was on the hilltop, the crow was in the hollow.

At night he perched on a tree, and directed her to go forward to a house.

This house she soon reached, and found in it only a woman who made her heartily welcome, and gave her a good supper, and a soft bed, where she slept a deep, tired sleep.

In the morning she told her story to this woman. And the woman pitied her, and gave her a comb, saying, "Any hair that is combed with this comb, will hang with pearls and jewels. It is called the

Comb of Plenty. Keep it, for it will yet be useful to you."

Maeve thanked her very heartily, and set out. She followed the crow once more; and when she was on the hilltop, he was in the hollow, and when she was in the hollow, he was on the hilltop.

But in the evening they reached a great hill, one side of which was bristling thick with harrow pins, and the other side with glass. And over this hill flew the crow.

Maeve tried to climb the Hill of Harrow Pins; but they rent her, and tore her, and pierced through her feet, until at last, all torn and worn, she threw herself at the bottom and began to cry in despair.

The Blacksmith of the Hill of Harrow Pins found her in this woeful state, and his wife bathed her, and dressed her, and cured her wounds. Then he bargained that if she would serve seven years' apprenticeship with him, he would shoe her so that she could walk up the Hill of Harrow Pins and down the Hill of Glass, and follow Cally Coo-Coo.

She agreed to this, served seven years to the Blacksmith of the Hill of Harrow Pins, and at the

end of that time he shod her, so that she climbed
the Hill of Harrow Pins and went down the Hill
of Glass, safe and unhurt. Away and away before
her she then traveled, over hill, height, and hollow, moor, mountain, and scrug, lone valley and
green glen—until at long and last, one day, she
reached a river which flowed by a beautiful castle.

At this river was gathered a crowd of women,
each of them in turn trying to wash a shirt. Maeve
asked the women what this meant, and they told
her that the Prince of the East, who lived in that
beautiful castle, had been a long time under enchantment far away; but had come home seven
years ago, a most beautiful young man. Since
then his people had tried to make him marry; but
he said he was married to a beautiful Princess in
Ireland, who was on her way after him. But
after they had waited seven years for their new
Queen to come, his people lost patience, and said
she must be dead or unfaithful, and would never
come, and that he must marry. He said she might
be dead, but not unfaithful. And when he could
hold out against his people no longer, he had given
out that whatever young woman would wash three

blood-stains from this shirt which was now in the river, should be his wife. But they said they must be enchanted blood-stains, for every woman there had tried, and none could wash them out.

"Let me try," said Maeve. And taking the shirt in her hands, with three rubs she washed away the blood-stains.

Then a coarse, big girl, named Eiver, who was there, struck her and stunned her, and knocked Maeve down; took the shirt and ran with it to the castle, saying she had washed out the blood-stains.

Now a good hen-wife, by the castle, had assured the Prince that no woman but his true wife could wash out these magic blood-stains, which had come on his shirt the night his bull's hide was burned. So, when this coarse girl appeared, and showed the spots washed out, and claimed the Prince, he was seized with a great sickness, and had to be carried to his bed. This girl, Eiver, insisted upon her right to nurse him, and was by his bed both day and night.

When Maeve recovered, the hen-wife took her home to her cottage, and kept her there.

After a little while the Prince began to get well, and it was announced that in three days more he would be married to Eiver, in accordance with his promise.

There was a slovenly and ill-cared-for scullion at the castle, whom Eiver sent to the hen-wife for some eggs. To her Maeve said: "Will you let me comb your hair for you?"

And when she combed the scullion's tattery head with the Comb of Plenty, the scullion returned to the castle with hair the most beautiful that had ever been seen, the ends of it hanging with pearls and jewels.

Eiver sent the scullion back to the hen-wife to ask what Maeve would take for the Comb.

Maeve said, "She can have the Comb, if she lets me nurse the Prince tonight."

This was agreed to, and the Comb of Plenty given to Eiver. But before she gave the Prince in charge to Maeve, Eiver gave him sleeping-drops, and turned his face to the wall.

All that night, Maeve, as she sat by his side and held his hand, sang to him, "Far hast thou brought me, far have I sought thee; two bonny children borne unto thee; and seven sore years to the Blacksmith served; I climbed up the Hill of

Harrow Pins, and down the Hill of Glass; and three drops of red blood washed from thy shirt. Won't my bonny, bonny husband turn unto me?" But from the deep-sleeping Prince, Maeve did not get one word until she left in the morning.

The next day, when the scullion came to the hen-wife's for eggs, her dress was all wretched and ragged and bad.

Maeve said, "Let me fix your dress for you." And taking her Needle of Beauty, Maeve put one stitch in the dress—and immediately the scullion was wearing one of the most beautiful silk dresses, sparkling with gold and silver spangles, that had ever been seen. And when the scullion returned to the castle, Eiver sent her back to inquire what Maeve would take for the Needle of Beauty.

Maeve said, "Permission to nurse the Prince one night."

This was agreed to. But as on the night before, Eiver gave the Prince sleep-drops, and turned his face to the wall, before Maeve got charge of him. And all that night Maeve held his hand and sang to him, "Far hast thou brought me, far have I sought thee; two bonny children borne unto thee; and seven sore years to the Blacksmith served; I

climbed up the Hill of Harrow Pins, and down
the Hill of Glass; and three drops of red blood
washed from thy shirt. Won't my bonny, bonny
husband turn unto me?" But not one word did
she get from the Prince until the day broke, and
she left.

On the next day, which was the Prince's wed-
ding-eve, the scullion was at the hen-wife's again.
She was a very, very ugly girl, with a very dirty
face.

Maeve said, "Let me wash your face for you."
And with one rub of the Towel of Loveliness on
the scullion's face, she left her the most beautiful
girl that had ever been seen. When the scullion
returned to the castle, Eiver sent her again to
the hen-wife's to ask what Maeve would take for
the Towel of Loveliness.

Maeve said, "One night to nurse the Prince,"
which was agreed to.

Now, the Prince had a faithful servant who
always slept in the next room. And this servant
had been kept awake the first night by Maeve's
singing all the night long to the sleeping Prince.
On the second night he had listened closely and
heard some of the words, and on this next day

told the Prince about it, and asked him what it meant.

The Prince was all astonished. He told the servant to say nothing more to any one until he would see. The Prince recollected that on the two nights past Eiver had made him take a drink before she left him. On this night when Eiver offered him a drink before she left him, he pretended to take it, but really spilled it between the bed and the wall. He then let on to go to sleep, with his face turned to the wall as usual.

When Maeve came in she sat down by his bedside as on the other nights, took hold of one of his hands, kissed it, and wept on it, and sang to him: Far hast thou brought me, far have I sought thee; two bonny children borne unto thee; and seven sore years to the Blacksmith served; I climbed up the Hill of Harrow Pins and down the Hill of Glass; and three drops of red blood washed from thy shirt. Won't my bonny, bonny husband turn unto me?"

As soon as she had finished, the Prince sat up and clasped her in his arms.

He had the whole castle roused at once. Eiver was called before him, and had to confess her falseness. She gave up the Needle of Beauty, the Towel of Loveliness, and the Comb of Plenty, and was banished from the country forever.

The preparations which were being made for the Prince's wedding the next day, were hurried now on a far greater scale—for his rewedding to Maeve. Invitations were sent east and west, north and south, to all the princes and lords and ladies, nobles and knights, of the land.

To the wedding came three strange women, who brought with them two very handsome little children, a boy and a girl. They were the three women who had housed and harbored Maeve in the woods, and the children were Maeve's own handsome boy, and beautiful girl—both of whom they handed over to their delighted mother.

A happier woman than Maeve was not that day in all the world, nor a happier man than the Prince of the East; nor a happier pair than they ever lived before or since.

THE HOUND OF THE HILL OF SPEARS

ONCE upon a time, there were a King and Queen of Ireland who had one son; and he was called Owen. The Queen died while Owen was very young, and the King married again. His new wife hated the boy, and did everything she could to annoy and hurt him, and drive him away. Owen, for his part, didn't mind her much, only went his own way.

He was very fond of fowling, and one day when out with his spear he followed far a beautiful blue hawk, the rarest ever he had seen. He did not catch it, but he brought home a feather that fell from its wing. And, as the feather was a pretty one, he showed it to all in the castle—his new mother among them. After supper that evening, his mother proposed that he should play a game of chess with her. He asked for what they should play; and she answered that whoever should win could put *geasa* * upon the other, to do anything commanded.

Owen agreed. And when they played he won the game. His stepmother was very much vexed at this. She asked him to play another game. Owen agreed again, but this time his stepmother won.

"Well," said Owen, "what *geasa* do you put on me?"

Said his mother: "The feather you brought home today was from the wing of the Blue Hawk of Connaught, which is owned by the Giant of the Seven Heads and Seven Trunks. All the world covets that Hawk; but though hundreds of champions have gone seeking it, none of them ever returned. The *geasa* I put upon you is to set out upon your travels and never return till you bring me the Blue Hawk of Connaught."

Poor Owen was sorely distressed by the terrible sentence. Said he, "For the game I won, the *geasa* I lay on you is that you stand upon the top of the tallest tower on my father's castle from the moment of my setting out till the hour of my returning with the Blue Hawk of Connaught. You

---

* An obligation of honor which no one can refuse or shun.

are to face the wind, and your food will be what seeds the wind blows you, and your drink the rain that falls on you."

His stepmother was enraged when she heard this. But she had to abide by her own bargain. And the next morning Owen, after bidding sad good-by to father and friends and every one in the castle, set out upon his travels. He saw his stepmother on the tallest tower facing the wind— there to remain, feeding on the seeds that were blown to her and drinking the rain, until he would return—if ever he would return—with the Blue Hawk of Connaught.

Far and far, and very far, poor Owen traveled, till, late that evening, as he sat down by the side of a little stream, weary and worn, and hungry, too, and was taking from his pocket a bit of oat-cake that he carried, down from the hills came bounding a beautiful white hound, which stood by and looked with hungry eyes at him eating his cake.

"I'm very, very hungry," said the hound. "Will you divide with me?"

"My poor hound," said Owen, "you surely cannot be half as hungry as myself."

But he divided his oat-cake, and gave half of it to the hound, which ate it greedily. Then it asked Owen what journey he was bent upon. And Owen told the hound his sad story.

"Poor Owen," said the hound, "it is sorry for you I am. You are going upon the most venturous, and most terrible task in all the world; but, if I can do anything to help you, I surely shall. Come with me this night anyhow, and rest yourself. They call me the White Hound of the Hill of Spears."

He thanked the hound, and away with it he went. And it brought him to a fine house on a hill, where Owen got a soft bed. And a sweet sleep he had there that night.

Next morning the White Hound spoke to him about the errand he was on, and told him how the Blue Hawk was guarded by the terrible Giant of the Seven Heads and Seven Trunks.

"I have lived on this hill for a hundred years," said the Hound, "and have seen nine-and-ninety brave heroes pass every year on the quest of the Blue Hawk, but none of them ever returned. However," said the Hound, "the Giant is just now in need of a boy to care for the Hawk, and your best plan is to offer him your service. When he asks what you can do, answer him that you are apt at anything you turn to, but especially handy at minding hawks. If you be lucky enough to get charge of the Hawk, be as kind to the bird as you can, till you make it grow to like you. If you succeed in this, it is well and very well—it may be that you will be able to get its consent to go away with you. But when you have got its consent, your terrible task is only begun: for every stone in the Giant's castle is enchanted, and can tell him if anything goes wrong. If he discovers you trying to steal the Blue Hawk, you cannot escape with your life. The Giant lives five thousand miles' journey from here; but if you look into my left ear you'll get a chip; which, when you take it out, will turn into a white rod. Strike me with the rod and I'll be a dappled steed, and then will quickly carry you to the Giant's castle."

Owen thanked the Hound right heartily. Out of its left ear he took a little chip, which turned into a rod in his hand. He struck the Hound with the rod, and lo! it was a beautiful dappled steed! Then, mounting the steed, he started off. Only the heels of his horse touched the tops of the hills, as they whirled over the world like a comet. They o'ertook the wind before them, but the wind behind couldn't o'ertake them.

And in the evening they reached the castle of the Giant of the Seven Heads and Seven Trunks. Dismounting, Owen struck the horse with the rod again, and turned it into the White Hound of the Hill of Spears once more. The Hound counselled and advised Owen again, and wished him success; and it said if he ever escaped from the Giant's castle with his life, it would be waiting here to help him. Owen thanked it right heartily, and bade it good-by.

Then he went up to the castle and knocked at the gates; and a Giant of Seven Heads and Seven Trunks, the most terrible Owen had ever seen, came out and asked who he was and what he wanted. He answered that he was Owen, the King of Ireland's son, and was a boy in search of a master. The Giant asked what he could do, and Owen answered that he was apt at anything he turned to, but especially handy at minding hawks.

"Very well," said the Giant, "as I'm just needing such a boy, I'll engage you for a bag of gold,

77

to serve me for a year and a day; and in the morning I'll show you your work."

He took Owen in, gave him supper and bed; and in the morning told him he was going to put his work before him.

To a tall tower in one corner of the castle, the Giant led Owen, and showed him the beautiful Blue Hawk, which he himself had followed in the forest not many days before.

"Your duty," said the Giant, "is to care for and feed that Hawk, and see that nothing happens to it." And he warned Owen that if he ever interfered with the Hawk or neglected his duty, he would immediately pay for it with his head. He then left Owen and the bird together.

At once Owen began being friendly with the bird. He was very good indeed to it, fed it on the best, and washed and sleeked it every morning, and saw that it never wanted for anything it desired.

Very well and good. The Hawk liked Owen from the first; and fonder of him it grew every day, till at last it consented to go off with him.

They planned to escape at twelve o'clock on a certain night. When the time came, through the

window both of them were getting, the bird under
Owen's arm, when the Hawk happened to flutter,
and the tip of its wing to touch a stone.

That instant the stone cried out, "Master!
Master! Master!" in a voice that could be heard
the distance of seven hills and seven dales. And
the next minute the Giant had overtaken and
caught Owen, and brought himself and the bird
back into the castle.

"Now," said the Giant, "your life is mine."

"All right," said Owen, "I'm willing to die."

"But wouldn't you like better to live?" said the
Giant.

"How do you mean?" said Owen.

The Giant said, "I only want one thing to make
me Master of the World—but that one thing I
have never yet been able to get. It is the Sword
of Light belonging to the King of Denmark, a
flash from which can light up half the world; and
which is in the innermost room of the King's
palace, and day and night guarded by ten thousand warriors. Hundreds of heroes have gone
seeking that Sword, but none ever returned with
his life. Your life," he said to Owen, "will be

spared if within a year and a day you bring me that wonderful Sword."

Owen said that worse than lose his life in the quest he could not; and he would have a try anyhow. So off he set on his adventure.

He had not gone far, when the White Hound of the Hill of Spears appeared, and asked him how he had fared. Poor Owen told what had happened; and the Hound said that it indeed pitied him, for that he was now going on a far more venturesome task than before. "But," said the Hound, "I'll do everything in my power to help you." It commanded Owen to take from its left ear the chip which should become a rod in his hand, and turn the Hound into a magnificent eagle.

Owen did as he was directed; then mounted upon the eagle's back, and started. The tips of the eagle's wings brushed the fire off the stars, as they went over the world like a comet. They o'ertook the whirlwinds before them, and the whirlwinds behind couldn't o'ertake them—and they never stopped or stayed till, late that evening, they alighted at the castle of the King of

Denmark. Here Owen turned the eagle into the Hound again.

The Hound advised Owen to ask for employment at the castle, and when the King should inquire what he could do, to answer that he was apt at anything he turned to, but especially handy at caring for swords. "He needs a man just now to mind the Sword of Light," said the Hound, "and may employ you. If you ever escape from the castle with your life, you'll find me here waiting for you."

Right heartily Owen thanked the Hound, and went up and knocked at the castle gates. The King himself it was who came out. And he asked Owen who he was and what he wanted. He answered that he was Owen, King of Ireland's son, and was looking for service. The King asked him what he could do, and Owen said he was apt at anything he turned to, but especially handy at caring for swords.

"Well," said the King, "I'm needing such a boy just now. And I'll give you a bag of gold to serve me for a year and a day. Come in, and in the morning I'll show you your work."

He brought Owen into the castle, gave him his

supper and a good bed that night; and the next morning he took him to the innermost room where the Sword of Light was kept. And though the room had neither window nor mousehole, it was as bright as dazzling day, because the Sword of Light was there shining.

Owen was put in charge of the Sword to mind and care for it; and warned that if anything happened to the Sword his life would pay the penalty.

Great care he surely took of it, polished it well and carefully every morning and night, and was never tired attending to it. At the end of a month, when he had got to know the Sword well, and had spied out all the secret ways of the palace, he made up his mind to escape with the sword. So at midnight one night, after a feast, when all the guards, having eaten and drunk too heartily, had fallen asleep, Owen took the Sword from its case, and was escaping by a window when the first flash from it lit up half the world, and wakened the King and the ten thousand guards, and every one in, and for a hundred miles around, the palace, with its fierce and fiery light. Owen was overtaken and brought back; and the King ordered him to be executed immediately.

"Is there no way at all in which I can save or earn my life?" said Owen.

"No way," said the King of Denmark, "but an impossible way."

"What do you mean?" said Owen.

Said the King of Denmark, "There is only one thing I want to make me Master of the World—and that is the wonderful Steed of Bells belonging to the King of Spain. Hundreds of heroes have set out to steal that Steed, but none ever came back with his life. I'll spare your life, if within a year and a day, you bring me the King of Spain's Steed of Bells."

"Well," said Owen, "if my life's to be lost, I may as well lose it in a good cause, anyhow. So I'll try; and, worse than fail I cannot do."

Off then he started; but he hadn't gone far when he found the White Hound awaiting him.

"What luck?" asked the White Hound.

And sorry was the Hound when he heard how Owen had fared and failed. And far sorrier still when he learnt the new task Owen had to perform. "For," said the Hound, "I'm afraid it's an impossible task. But, all the same, I'll do what I can to help you."

83

He had Owen strike him with the rod, and thereby turn him into a ship in full sail. And getting Owen aboard, the ship started, and o'ertook the wind before, while the wind behind couldn't o'ertake it—till at last they ran ashore under the castle of the King of Spain.

"Go up to the castle," said the Hound, "and ask for employment. As luck would have it, the King is just now seeking for a trusty man to mind and tend the Steed of Bells. When he asks what you can do, say you are apt at anything, but particularly good at minding horses. If he employs you, you may have a chance in a million of stealing the Steed. If you escape alive you'll find me here waiting to aid you."

Right heartily Owen thanked the Hound, and went off to the castle.

The King himself came out, and asked Owen who he was and what he wanted. The youth answered that he was Owen, the son of the King of Ireland, and was traveling in search of employment. The King asked him what he could do, and Owen replied that he was apt at anything, but particularly good at minding horses. Then the King said he was just now in need of a boy for minding a particular horse; and that he would give Owen a bag of gold, if he served him faithfully for a year and a day.

"Come inside," said the King, "and in the morning I'll show you your duties."

Owen, nothing loath, went in, had a good supper, a soft bed, and a sweet sleep. And in the morning, the King showed him the Steed of Bells, which had a gorgeous stable all to itself, and told him it was the most wonderful steed in all the world, and that champions from the earth's ends had come trying to steal this animal, but that the minute they laid hand on him, the thousand bells with which he was decked, rang, and their ringing was heard round half the world. And that consequently no man could steal the Steed—but all lost their lives in the attempt. So with many warnings, the King left the Steed in Owen's care.

Owen was particularly kind to the Steed of Bells, watched it, and cared for it, and groomed it, and fed it well—hoping to win it by his kindness. And, indeed, in a short time he and the Steed were great friends, surely. He wasn't a month with the King of Spain when he had made up with the Steed of Bells to take it away; and the Steed of Bells was right willing to go with him, so dearly did it love Owen.

So in the middle of a night, when the King and his court and all the guards were sleeping heavily after a feast, Owen got up and roused the Steed of Bells, and started off with it. But just as he was getting out of the castle gate, didn't one of the bells touch the gate—and that moment all the thousand bells upon the Steed rang out so loud that they were heard round half the world. The King and his court and all the world woke up; and Owen was seized, and led into the castle again and the Steed of Bells safely stabled.

And then the King told poor Owen that he had earned his death, as many a reckless fellow had done before.

"Is there no chance for my life?" Owen asked.

"There's one," said the King, "but it is an impossible one."

"Anyhow," said Owen, "let me hear what it is."

"It is," said the King, "that you steal for me, and bring me here, within a year and a day, Starlight, the beautiful daughter of the King of Greece. I only need Starlight for my wife, that I may be Master of the World. Thousands of champions from all parts of the world have gone to Greece on the same errand, but not one has ever lived to return."

"Well," said Owen, "one other life cannot much matter; and, worse than fail I cannot do."

Then the King parted with Owen; and Owen went down to the sea, where he found the White Hound of the Hill of Spears awaiting him. When the Hound heard how he had fared, he was right sorry. "But," said the Hound, "I'll do all I can for you, anyhow."

So by the Hound's directions Owen turned it into a tremendous whale. Owen got on its back, and started for Greece. They swept the ocean like a whirlwind. They o'ertook the mad waves before them, and the mad waves behind couldn't o'ertake them—till at length they ran into the harbor by the castle of the King of Greece.

Here the Hound was turned again from a whale to a beautiful ship.

By the advice of the White Hound, Owen decided to invite the King of Greece to come down and taste some of the fine wines he had brought from Spain.

"If he consents to come," said the Hound, "he'll

bring with him his beautiful daughter, Starlight. And then it will be for you to win her heart and steal her if you can; and I'll quickly carry you both to Spain."

When the King of Greece heard that the King of Ireland's son was in the harbor, and wished him to come and taste his Spanish wines, he came at once with all his court, amongst them his beautiful daughter, Starlight, with whom Owen fell instantly in love. Owen feasted them right royally on board the ship, and gave them the choicest of the sweet wines of Spain; and asked them to come again as often as they wished.

In the harbor he lay for three weeks, and the King and his court came often to chat with him, and drink the wines of Spain. And every time they came, they brought the beautiful Starlight, with whom Owen was able to get in a few words. And every succeeding time he saw her he loved her more and more deeply. And, indeed, it was plain to be seen that Starlight was each time getting fonder and fonder of Owen—for he was a handsome, brave fellow.

At length he persuaded her to come down to the ship one day with only her guardian lady, that they might have a sail in the harbor. But when Owen got them aboard, behold, he started the ship at full speed, and headed for Spain.

Soon the news spread that Owen had carried off the King's beautiful daughter, and the King had his swiftest boats launched, and away in pursuit. But though they sailed at their swiftest, Owen's boat outdistanced them far, and they had to return sorrowfully home.

But little sorry was Starlight to be carried away by one whom she loved as she did Owen, the King of Ireland's son.

When they reached Spain, and got on dry land, just by the King's castle, and when the ship was again turned into the White Hound of the Hill of Spears, the Hound asked Owen to strike him with the wand. Owen did so, and the Hound became a most beautiful young lady, the picture of Starlight, the daughter of the King of Greece. So much alike were they that, seeing both of them standing together, Owen could not tell the real Starlight from the White Hound. By the Hound's directions, Owen left the real Starlight with her guardian in a cave on the seashore, and took the enchanted one with him to the castle of the King of Spain, and handed her over to the King, who was overjoyed, and gave Owen his release and bestowed on him the Steed of Bells into the bargain. "For," the King said, "by your heroism well have you earned it."

With the Steed of Bells Owen went to the seashore, and there waited with Starlight till evening, when the Hound, having cast a sleeping spell on every one in the castle and escaped, came trotting in his own shape to the shore. Here the Hound changed itself into a ship, Owen got aboard with the beautiful Princess and her guardian, and the Steed of Bells, and went on the wind's wings to Denmark.

Having landed by the castle of the King of Denmark, the ship turned into a Hound, and the Hound into a Steed of Bells, the very picture of the real Steed of Bells of the King of Spain. And Owen, leaving the real Steed of Bells with Starlight, by the shore, went to the castle with the enchanted Steed of Bells. Great was the joy of the King of Denmark to get the Steed of Bells he had so long coveted. He joyfully gave Owen his release, and bestowed on him the Sword of Light in reward for his valiant daring.

To the shore, then, went Owen, and waited with Starlight and the real Steed of Bells, till the enchanted Steed, having cast a sleeping spell over the court of the King of Denmark and escaped, came trotting down to them. Here it changed itself into a ship, and Owen got on board with the Princess and her friend, and the Steed of Bells, and the Sword of Light. They swept like the sunlight over the waters until they came to the coast of Connaught—where they landed, just by the castle of the Giant of the Seven Heads and the Seven Trunks, who owned the Blue Hawk of Connaught.

Here the White Hound, again giving directions to Owen, changed itself into a Sword of Light, the very picture of the real one. Leaving the real Sword with the Steed and Starlight, on the shore, Owen took the enchanted one to the castle of the Giant. And when the Giant appeared Owen handed him the Sword and asked for his release. This the Giant joyfully gave him, and besides, bestowed on him the Blue Hawk of Connaught as a reward for his heroism. He was overjoyed to get the Sword of Light. For now, he

91

said, he could destroy all his enemies, and be Master of the World.

Owen, with the Blue Hawk, went off to the shore and there waited with his companions.

And behold! in the middle of the night didn't the enchanted Sword arise and cut off the Heads of the Giant of the Seven Heads and Seven Trunks, the tyrant who tyrannized over the world —and then return, in its hound shape, to Owen and his companions. Then Owen, with Starlight, the Steed of Bells, the Sword of Light, the Blue Hawk, and the White Hound, set out for his father's castle.

"And now," said the White Hound, "as you are near home, and safe and successful, I have one favor to ask from you."

Said Owen, "Name any favor in the whole world that it is in my power to grant—and it will be yours. For to you I owe everything."

Said the White Hound, "The favor I ask is that you will cut off my head with the Sword of Light."

"That is something I will never do, my best of friends," said Owen, sorrowfully.

But the White Hound insisted. And it assured

Owen that instead of its harming the Hound, it would be its saving. So Owen, at last persuaded, cut off the Hound's head with the Sword of Light. And that instant the Hound changed into a most handsome young man.

"It was by enchantment," said the young man, "that I was the White Hound of the Hill of Spears. France is my country, and I'm the son of France's King. It was my father's enemy who laid the cruel spell upon me, from which I could never be freed till my Hound's head was cut off by the Sword of Light. That Sword could never have been got but by you. If I have been good to you, you have been still better to me. To you and your beautiful Princess, I wish every blessing that can come. I will bid good-by to you now, and be off to my own country, where a winsome Princess has been seven years awaiting me."

Owen and his beautiful Starlight went forward, then, with the Steed of Bells, the Sword of Light, and the Blue Hawk of Connaught.

When at length he sighted his father's castle, he saw his stepmother standing on the topmost tower, with her face to the wind, living on what grains the wind blew to her, and drinking the rain that fell on her. When she caught sight of Owen returning, and saw with him the Blue Hawk of Connaught, which was perched on his shoulder, she gave out of her a scream that rang three times round the world, fell from the tower, and was instantly killed on the flags below.

Out to meet Owen went his father all joyful, and the gentlemen and ladies of the court dancing with delight to welcome him—for sorely they had missed one whom they loved so well. And equally as warm was the welcome they, one and all, put before his beautiful Starlight.

Owen and Starlight were wedded. And the wedding festivities, the greatest ever known, lasted nine days and nine nights; and the last day and night's feasting were finer than the first. His father resigned the throne to Owen, who, possessed of his most beautiful Queen, his Sword of Light, his Steed of Bells, and his Blue Hawk of Connaught, lived and died the greatest King, and the happiest, that Ireland and the world ever knew.

THE BLACK SHEEP

ONCE upon a time, in the good old times of faraway and long ago, there were a King and a Queen of Donegal who had one beautiful daughter, named Ethna. But the Queen died, and the King married another Queen, who had three daughters of her own, as ugly as they were bold. And she and her daughters were bad and cruel to Ethna— even while her father lived. And when he died, they treated her still worse.

Ethna was so beautiful that every young man who came to the house fell in love with her; whilst no one could love or like her stepmother's ugly daughters. And this it was that made them so very, very hard upon Ethna.

To make Ethna ugly, her mother half-starved her. But instead of getting ugly, it was still lovelier she grew every day.

Then her mother and stepsisters consulted, and

said they would send her to herd the sheep on the hills, with nothing to eat from the time she left in the morning till she got home at night; and then the hunger and the harsh winds would soon take the beauty off her.

On the first day poor Ethna was on the hills herding, she grew very, very hungry in the middle of the day; and thinking of how she'd get nothing to eat till late at night, and maybe very little then, she sat down on a rock and cried.

From a flock that were grazing near, one little black sheep raised its head and looked at her; and then came walking up and rubbed its cheek against her cheek.

"Little Black Sheep," said Ethna, "what do you want with me?"

"Look in my left ear," said the little Black Sheep. "See what you'll see—and then help yourself."

Ethna looked into the Black Sheep's left ear, and there she got a wee napkin, which she took out and spread on the grass at her feet. And, behold you, it was a big tablecloth, and was instantly covered with all sorts to eat and drink— hams, jams, and clams, meats, sweets and Billy

Boleros—a finer spread than ever she had seen in her father's castle. Poor Ethna fell to, and made a right hearty meal.

When she had finished, the Black Sheep told her to roll up the napkin again, and put it where she got it. She rolled it up into a very small bulk again, and put it into the Sheep's left ear—and the Sheep took its place in the flock again, and began to graze, leaving Ethna very, very happy indeed.

When she came home, her mother and step-sisters asked her how she liked to be herding on the hill, and Ethna said she liked it very well indeed. And they were sorely disappointed.

The next day at noon, as she sat herding on the hill, and was beginning to feel very hungry entirely, the Black Sheep came up and told her to look in its left ear again, and see what she would see, and take it out and help herself. There she saw the napkin, which she took out and spread upon the grass. And it was, that minute, a big tablecloth, covered with all sorts of good things to eat and drink—hams, jams, and clams, meats, sweets and Billy Boleros—a finer spread than she had seen in her father's castle. Poor Ethna fell to, and made a right hearty meal indeed, that day also.

And after she had eaten and drunk to her hearty content, she rolled up the napkin and put it in the Sheep's ear again—and the Black Sheep went back to graze among the flock.

She had a very happy time on the hill; and when she came home, her mother and sisters asked her how she liked to be herding on the hill. And she said she never was so happy in her life. And they were sorely disappointed.

Every night they were looking to see her growing coarser and uglier; but instead, every night she came home looking finer and rosier and more beautiful than before. Right angry they grew, and wondered what was happening on the hill that made Ethna so happy. Among themselves they consulted and called in an old hen-wife, who advised that the eldest daughter should go to the hill next day to spy upon Ethna. And for that purpose the hen-wife turned the eldest into a pigeon.

When Ethna was taking the napkin out of the Black Sheep's ear this day, the Sheep said: "Look into my right ear, also, and take out what you will get there."

Out of its right ear Ethna took a chip, which turned into a rod in her hand.

"Now," said the Black Sheep, "when you are eating your dinner a pigeon will come hopping up beside you. You must strike it with that white rod."

And when Ethna was eating her dinner, as the Black Sheep had told, a pigeon alighted and came hopping up beside her. She struck it with the white rod, and it turned into a stone.

When she went home that night, she found only two stepsisters there—and they turned very black looks on her.

Among themselves they consulted again, and called in the hen-wife, who advised sending the second sister to the hill next day, in the shape of a magpie, to spy upon Ethna, and also to find out what had happened to their eldest sister.

On the next day, when Ethna was taking the napkin from the Black Sheep's ear, the little Sheep asked her to look into his right ear, and take out what she would find. And from his right ear, she took out a white chip, which turned into a rod in her hand.

The Black Sheep said, "When you are eating your dinner, a magpie will alight and hop up beside you. You must strike it with that rod."

And, sure enough, when Ethna was eating her dinner, near her there lit a magpie, which came hopping up beside her. She raised the rod and struck it, and it turned into a stone.

And that night, when she reached home, she found only one stepsister there with her mother —and both of them were in red wrath with her.

They called in the hen-wife, and it was agreed that the youngest sister should go to the hill next day in the shape of a crow. But the hen-wife warned her to fly over Ethna's head and watch all that would happen, but on no account to alight.

When at midday Ethna was taking from the little Sheep's ear the napkin, it told her to take the white rod from its right ear, and strike the crow that should alight beside her.

Ethna took the white rod. And when she was eating her dinner, she saw a crow flying around and around above her, but never alighting. She folded up the napkin after she had finished, and put it into the Sheep's left ear, and put the little white rod into its right ear, and the Sheep went away.

The crow was home before she came that night, and dark indeed were the looks her stepmother and stepsister greeted Ethna with when she arrived.

They consulted once more with the hen-wife as to what was best to do. They would have liked to kill Ethna, but were afraid; and the hen-wife advised them, since they would not kill her, to kill her friend, the Black Sheep, and to be sure to burn its bones.

On the next day, when the Black Sheep had come to her, and she had eaten a hearty meal and put back the napkin, the Black Sheep told Ethna what had happened, and that it was going to be killed, and that the hen-wife had ordered its bones to be burned.

"But I want you," it said to Ethna, "to gather up every one of my bones, before they get a chance of burning them, and throw them down the deep well in your garden."

As well you may suppose, poor Ethna was very, very sorry when she heard the Black Sheep was going to be killed. She promised faithfully that she would do what the Black Sheep wanted. And then she sat upon the hill crying bitterly all the remainder of the evening.

That night, by her stepmother's orders, she herself had to drive the Black Sheep home from the hill. The mother had it killed, and ordered every bone to be burned.

Now, the man that brought the bones to the fire was one whom Ethna had often fed from the kitchen. From him she begged the bones; and he gave them to her. She was carrying them to the well in the garden, when lo! didn't a dog run up and snatch a shin-bone from her, and run off with it. And poor Ethna cried sorely; but there was nothing for her to do but throw the rest of the bones down the well—which she did.

But behold! now the Sheep was killed, didn't the two stepsisters return home from the hills, their enchantment gone!

Then her stepmother put her into the kitchen again, to work with dirty pots and pans, and kept her there a long time, letting her see no one. Until at length the Princes who frequented the house forgot all about her.

THE BLACK SHEEP

Now the King of Ireland had a son who soon came of age to marry. His father announced three great balls to be given at his castle; and to these balls were invited all the eligible young women of the Kingdom, that the Prince might choose a wife for himself, from amongst them.

As well you may suppose, the hearts began fluttering of all the lovely girls between the four seas of Ireland. And for these balls wonderful preparations were made by all the young ladies of the Kingdom who thought they were handsome. For months and months before the balls came off, nothing was done but making and fitting dresses, and sewing on to them gold and silver braids, and jeweled ornaments, to make their owners look dazzling to the young Prince.

Ethna's stepsisters and stepmother weren't idle now. For all these months their house was turned upside down by the preparations they were making for captivating the young Prince. And each one of the sisters thought that she would surely win him. For every one of them thought herself the most beautiful girl, instead of one of the ugliest, in Erin.

They had to call in Ethna to help them; for,

much as they hated her, they knew well that her good taste in dress far surpassed theirs.

And when Ethna was helping them with their lovely dresses, they would pity her, saying, "Poor Ethna, pity that you can have no chance for the lovely young Prince."

And Ethna sighed and said nothing.

The night of the first big ball at length arrived. And when Ethna saw her stepmother and her three stepsisters depart in all their grandeur, she went back to the kitchen, sat down among the pots with her head in her hands, and began to cry bitterly.

Then she heard a voice in her ear saying, "What's the matter with you, little Ethna?"

And looking up she saw the Black Sheep, on three legs, standing by her side. And it was Ethna was the happy girl to see her old friend again, especially now in her distress. Only, she was grieved to see the Black Sheep limping on three legs, and asked where was its other leg. The Black Sheep said that was the bone the dog had taken away, but told her not to mind that. "But tell me why you are crying," said the Black Sheep.

Poor Ethna took in her arms the little Black

Sheep's head, and said how very, very sorry she was about losing the bone. And she then told the Sheep her own grief.

Said the Black Sheep: "Put your hand into my left ear and take out what you will find there."

And Ethna drew from the Sheep's left ear a white chip that instantly became a rod in her hands.

Said the Black Sheep: "At the foot of your garden there are three white rocks. Go to them, and strike them with that rod, when three doors will open in them. Go inside them, and fit yourself in the finest, for the Prince's ball. Enjoy yourself there, but be sure to leave before the company breaks up, and be back in your place in the kitchen again before your mother and sisters come home."

Then the Black Sheep disappeared, and Ethna went down the garden, struck the three white rocks, and three doors opened in them.

She went into the first, and there found a great, beautiful bright room, all hung round with the most dazzling dresses she had ever beheld in her life. In a short time she had one of the loveliest dresses there upon her.

Then she went into the next rock, and found it
filled with jewels and pearls, and gold and silver
ornaments, beyond wonder and count. She helped
herself to all of these that she wanted.

Into the third rock then she went, and found
there a stable filled with the handsomest horses
that ever champed a bit. She saddled the most
dashing of these steeds, took it out, mounted it,
and rode off to the ball.

And this was the appearance of Ethna arriving
at the ball: On her neat sweet feet she had a
slipper of gold and a slipper of silver, with jeweled buckles and pearled bows; a stocking of gold
and a stocking of silver, all glistening with diamonds beyond value; and she wore a snow-white
silk gown. Her ten fingers dripped honey, and
the nine birds of love were caroling above her
handsome head. Her hair fell in bonny brown
braids to her trim, slim waist; like lilies and
roses were her lovely cheeks; her eyes more beautiful than the skies, and her voice like the tinkling
of a silver bell. And she was mounted on a sleek,
slender brown steed that was swifter than the
wind.

There was great sensation when she arrived, and

every one at the ball thronged out to see the wonderful beauty who had come, from no one knew where.

Six Princes struggled to see which would help her to alight, but the young Prince of Ireland, coming out, insisted upon his right to do so. He lifted her to the ground, and gave the slender brown steed that was swift as the wind into the charge of one of his men-in-waiting.

The sensation grew still greater when, in the ballroom, they beheld this lovely unknown damsel open the ball with Ireland's beautiful young Prince—for so elegant a dancer or so beautiful a damsel no one there had ever seen before.

But lo! before the ball was ended, Ethna slipped away; and with her ten fingers dripping honey, and the nine birds singing over her handsome head, her slipper of gold and her slipper of silver, with their jeweled buckles and pearled bows, her stocking of gold and stocking of silver, glistening with diamonds, and her snow-white silk gown, she rode home on her sleek, slender brown steed, which was faster than the wind.

When she reached home, she laid away her dress and her ornaments and her steed where she got them; and the rocks closed behind her. Then, in her old tattered torn dress, she was sitting in the kitchen among the pots when her stepmother and stepsisters came bursting into the house, returned from the ball.

They were talking and talking at a great rate, and Ethna asked them what was the news from the ball, and whom had the young Prince fancied.

"What need you care about the young Prince, or whom he fancied!" they answered her. But still they couldn't help telling her of the dazzling damsel, who had come from no one knew where, whose gorgeous beauty had bewitched the Prince and every one there, but who had slipped away and disappeared before the ball was over.

The second ball was to come off a week later, and for this there were greater preparations than before. Ethna helped to dress her stepsisters, and they pitied poor Ethna who couldn't see the beautiful ball, and the beautiful Prince, and stand a chance of the Prince's hand.

But when they had gone to the ball, as Ethna sat in the kitchen, her friend, the Black Sheep, came hopping in on three legs.

She welcomed it, and kissed it.

THE BLACK SHEEP

The Black Sheep asked Ethna to put her hand into its left ear, and take out what she would find. She took out a chip which turned into a white rod. Then he told her to go to the three rocks at the garden's foot, strike them with the white rod, and help herself—and go to the ball—but to be sure to come away before the ball was over.

To the foot of the garden Ethna went, struck the three rocks, went in and dressed and decorated herself, mounted the steed and rode off to the ball.

And Ethna, arriving at the King of Ireland's castle, had on her neat, sweet feet a slipper of gold and a slipper of silver, with buckles of jewels, and bows of pearls; a stocking of gold and a stocking of silver, all glistening with diamonds; and she wore a snow-white silk gown. Her ten fingers dripped honey, and the nine birds of love were caroling above her handsome head. Her hair fell in bonny brown braids to her trim slim waist; like lilies and roses were her lovely cheeks; her eyes more beautiful than the skies, and her voice like the tinkling of a silver bell. And she was mounted on a sleek, slender brown steed that was swifter than the wind.

There was a great sensation this night again, when it was told that the beautiful damsel was arriving, and all who were at the ball rushed out to see her. Twelve Princes struggled to help her to alight, but the young Prince of Ireland, coming out, insisted on his right to help her off—which he did—and gave the slender brown steed in charge of a man-in-waiting.

He led her in, and with her opened the ball. And all the people there were in a state of the greatest wonder and admiration at the loveliness of this strange, beautiful damsel, whom nobody knew, and who, if she looked lovely the first night, looked twice as lovely now.

All that night, the young Prince paid to the other lovely young women there only as much attention as good manners demanded, but he was by Ethna's side every moment he could be.

Suddenly, however, they all missed her. For she had slipped away, mounted her slender brown steed, and with her ten fingers dripping honey, and the nine birds singing over her handsome head, rode for home as swift as the wind. She stabled the slender brown steed in his rock again, changed her clothes, and was sitting in the kitchen among the pots, when her mother and sisters came home, full of wonder and loud chatter.

Ethna asked them for news of the ball and the Prince. And they said, "What need you care about balls and Princes!" But they couldn't help telling her all about the dazzling damsel who had appeared and fascinated the young Prince, as well as every one else there, and who had as suddenly disappeared again.

Well and good. The third ball was to come off a week later. Ethna helped to dress and deck her sisters for this one also, and they pitied her very much because she wouldn't get a chance of seeing the ball, and seeing the beautiful Prince, and having a chance for his hand.

After they and their mother had gone off to the ball the Black Sheep appeared to Ethna, hopping in upon three legs. Ethna hugged and kissed the poor Black Sheep. And out of his ear she again got the white rod, with all directions. To the garden she went, and struck the rocks and opened the chambers and entered, and dressed and fitted herself out, and mounted her steed.

And this was the appearance of Ethna, riding to the Prince of Ireland's ball. She had on her neat sweet feet a slipper of gold and a slipper of silver, with buckles of jewels and bows of pearls; a stocking of gold and a stocking of silver, glistening with diamonds, and she wore a snow-white silk gown. Her ten fingers dripped honey, and the nine birds of love were caroling above her handsome head. Her hair fell in bonny brown braids to her trim slim waist; like lilies and roses were her lovely cheeks; her eyes more beautiful than the skies, and her voice like the tinkling of a silver bell. And she was mounted on a sleek, slender brown steed that was swifter than the wind.

As she rode up to the castle, all the crowds of people who had come to the ball turned out to see, and twenty Princes struggled to help her to alight. But the Prince of Ireland himself came out, and insisted on his right to do so. He helped her off, gave her steed in charge of the men-in-waiting, led her in, and opened the ball with ther.

If Ethna looked beautiful on the other two nights, she looked ten times more beautiful this time. Anything to equal her beauty no one there had ever seen, heard, or thought of. And every one was lost in wonder and amazement.

The young Prince, it was plain, was very, very much in love with this lovely maiden. And he watched her, and waited on her, and walked after her wherever she went through the room—resolved not to let her out of his sight. Before the ball broke up, however, she slipped away, and mounted her steed.

But the Prince, watching her more closely this night, dashed after her from the hall, and discovered her mounting. She put spurs to her horse when she saw him coming, and her horse leaped off. The Prince gave a quick bound after, and tried to get hold of her, but only got hold of her golden slipper. It came away in his hand. And on her slender brown steed she rode off, her ten fingers dripping honey, and nine birds singing over her handsome head, and she went home as swift as the wind.

She was in the kitchen, dressed in her old torn dress, among the pots and pans, when her mother and sisters returned from the ball. They were full of excitement, talking all together at the top of their voices, and Ethna asked them what was the news of the Prince and the ball.

"Ah," they said, "what need you care!"

But they couldn't help telling her of the wonderful happenings of the night, and of how the Prince had watched the strange damsel when she tried to steal off on her steed; how he had grabbed at her, but only got hold of her golden slipper. And he had given out, they said, that he would travel all his kingdom to find the maiden whom the slipper fitted. And that girl he was to marry. Each thought there was hope for her, for, by hook or by crook, she would make the slipper fit her.

On the very next day, the young Prince of Ireland, with half a dozen other Princes, set out to try the slipper on all the maidens in Ireland.

He traveled before him far, far and far, trying the slipper on every girl whom he met. The slipper was very, very dainty indeed, and few girls had a foot small enough to fit it. But, everywhere he went, the girls nipped and clipped their feet, and pressed and bound them up, to make them fit the slipper. Still, no one of them would it fit.

At length, the Prince and his retinue were due to reach the house of Ethna's stepmother and try it upon the maidens there.

They had made mighty preparations for his coming, and had their feet in bonds for a fortnight, hoping to make the slipper fit. They said it would be a shame to let him see dirty, tattered young Ethna, so they hid her under a cateran hide in the corner.

When the Prince at last arrived, every one of the girls had on her sweetest way; every one offered to try on the slipper, and every one of them nipped and clipped and pressed and bound her foot trying to get it in.

In a thorn-tree that grew by the window a robin all at once began to sing:

> *"Nippet foot and clippet foot*
> *Behind the Prince would ride,*
> *But bonny foot and handsome foot*
> *Under the cateran hide."*

"What is the robin saying?" asked the Prince.
"Oh, some nonsensical rhyme," the mother said, throwing a stone at the robin and driving it away.

After they had all tried, and tried again, not one of them could fit her foot to the slipper. And the Prince asked was there no other girl in the house.

The girls and their mother said there was no other.

But the robin had returned to the thorn-tree, and was singing:

> *"Nippet foot and clippet foot*
> *Behind the Prince would ride,*
> *But bonny foot and handsome foot*
> *Under the cateran hide."*

"What is that robin singing?" asked the Prince.

"Oh, some nonsensical rubbish," they said, throwing a stone at the robin, and driving it away again.

"Well," said the Prince, "I must be going."

And off he started.

As he went down the avenue, he saw the robin perched on a bush before him; and as he was curious, he asked of the robin, "What was it that you were singing at the window?"

And then the robin sang:

> *"Nippet foot and clippet foot*
> *Behind the Prince would ride,*
> *But bonny foot and handsome foot*
> *Under the cateran hide."*

The Prince at once turned back, went to the room again, searched it, and found poor ragged

Ethna hidden under a cateran hide in the corner.

He ordered her to come out and try on the slipper. And when Ethna tried, it slipped on her at once and fitted her like a glove.

The Prince, rejoiced, ordered her to prepare to go with him.

Ethna begged for time to dress. She ran down the garden, where the little Black Sheep was now waiting for her. Out of his ear she took the white rod, struck the rocks, and went in, dressed, mounted the steed, and came to the Prince.

And this was how Ethna appeared, when the King, overjoyed, beheld her.

She had on her neat sweet feet a slipper of gold and a slipper of silver, with buckles of jewels, and bows of pearls; a stocking of gold, and a stocking of silver, glistening with diamonds, and she wore a snow-white silk gown. Her ten fingers dripping honey, and the nine birds of love were caroling above her handsome head. Her hair fell in bonny brown braids to her trim slim waist; like lilies and roses were her lovely cheeks; her eyes more beautiful than the skies, and her voice like the tinkling of a silver bell. And she was mounted on a sleek, slender brown steed, that was swifter than the wind.

And anything half so fair or beautiful, the young Prince, or any other of the young Princes with him, had never seen or dreamed of in all their lives before.

Off with them she rode, to the King's castle, where they were wedded. The wedding lasted seven days and seven nights, each day and night better than the one before, and the last day and night better and greater than all the others put together.

The King of Donegal gave his son half his kingdom, and, a happy King and Queen, the Prince and Ethna ruled during all their long, bright lives after.

THE WEE RED MAN

T WAS in the faraway of long ago, when the world was rare and happenin's quarer, a thousand times than they are today, that this befell.

'Twas in Donegal there fought and wrought against Fate, the world, and the divil, one Conal O'Donnell, a blacksmith by trade, and as honest and kindly a craiture as the dogs ever barked at. But after a wrastle and a tussle, that lasted for years, the world and the divil got the better of Conal, and laid him out flat as a pancake, an' as poor as a Feb'uary snipe. There was one morning at last, he got up out of his bed, without the makin's of a meal in the house, his mealchest as empty as a school on Sunday, no morsel in the cupboard, and his pocket without power to produce a jingle, though he should dance the Highland-fling.

Downhearted he walked out of his house and stood him at the door of his blacksmith's forge, adjoinin', with his shoulder against the jamb of the door, his arms crossed, and his eyes and his heart at his feet, both of them. When all at once he heard a clatter of a horse, and liftin' his eyes, he beheld, ridin' up the road, a little red man upon a little pony.

The Little Red Man drew in with a "God save ye, Conal O'Donnell!"

"Save yourself," says Conal, givin' back the courtesy. "Is it anything I can do for you?"

"Would you lend me," says the Little Red Man, "the loan of your forge fire for a wheen o' minutes till I shoe my horse?"

"With a heart and a half," says Conal O'Donnell, who was always the heart and soul of a good fellow.

"And would you lend me," says the Little Red Man, "the loan of a carvin' knife?"

Now Conal O'Donnell, in all his born days, had never before heard of a horse being shod with a carvin' knife. But he was too polite to question a stranger; so a carvin' knife he fetched in a jiffy. Then on a big stone, that stood by the forge door, the Little Red Man sharpened his carvin' knife, sharpened it up, and sharpened it up, and sharpened it up, till he could only afford to finger the edge very jinteely. Then the Little Red Man went over to his pony, cut the four legs off him at the knees, gathered them up in his arms, and stuck them into the forge fire, and covered them up with coals.

"Conal O'Donnell," says the Little Red Fellow, "could you kindly blow the bellows for me?"

Now Conal was all dumbfoundered at this new way of shoeing a horse. But he was too polite to question a stranger. So the bellows he blew and blew, workin' them like a Connaughtman, and sending up the flames like a fury.

And when at length he thought the four legs must be burned to a cinder, the Little Red Fellow says, "I think they're done, now."

And goin' over to the fire, and rakin' the coals aside, he lifts out in his arms, lo and behold ye, four new legs with a new set of shoes on the ends of them—goes out and sticks the four legs under the pony, and jumpin' on the pony's back, says, "Good-mornin' to ye, thank ye, and good luck to ye, Conal O'Donnell!" and rides off.

Poor Conal, all dumbfoundered, stood like a stone statue in his forge door, lookin' after the Little Red Fellow, and when his speeches returned to him, "Well, that's the wonderfullest way," says he, "and the convenientest that I ever heard tell, of shoeing a horse. It's wish I do that I had known that way thirty years ago, and 'tis the rich man I'd now be entirely."

The words weren't well out of Conal when, behold ye, he heard the clatter of a horse again, and lookin' down the road, who should he see come ridin' up but the King of Ireland himself, upon a beautiful dancin', prancin', yellow steed.

And when the King of Ireland got as far as the forge, he reined in his beautiful, dancin', prancin', yellow steed and says, "Good-mornin', Conal O'Donnell!"

"Good-mornin', King of Ireland!" says Conal, says he. "Is it anythin' I can do for ye?"

"Ye can shoe my horse for me," says the King of Ireland, jumpin' off his steed, and throwin' the reins to Conal, "and I'll be forever grateful. And while you're shoein' him I think I'll take a wander up the hill here, and look around upon my kingdom, to see if it is all there, yet. Take good care of my steed," says he, "because he's the valubelest in Ireland, and you might leg it all the way to Australia and home again, without meetin' up with his likes."

"The best of care he'll get at my hands," says Conal, says he, leadin' him into the forge, as the King went strollin' up the hill.

Then Conal went out to the house to look for a carvin' knife—to try the new way of shoeing a horse. Upon a stone by the forge door he sharpened the carvin' knife till he had a jinteel edge upon it, then makin' up to the King of Ireland's beautiful dancin', prancin', yellow steed he cut the four legs off him at the knees, and slipped them into the forge fire, and covered them up with coals. To the bellows then he went, and worked them like a Connaughtman, while the flames went up like fury. And when at length he thought they were done, he went to the fire, and raked the coals aside. And, behold ye, when he raked the coals aside, there wasn't anything left there but cinders.

Through the forge door he beheld the King of Ireland comin' down the hill again to get his beautiful dancin', prancin', yellow steed, which was now lying there with divil a leg to him.

"Och, och," says Conal, says he, throwin' up his hands, " 'tis behead me the King of Ireland'll do for slayin' his beautiful steed!" And jumpin' out of the back window, he ran for the woods.

When the King of Ireland entered the forge, and beheld the spectacle that met his astonished eyes, he began dancin' like a madman.

But before many hours he had the whole of his army and half of his butlers screenging the country, to fetch him Conal O'Donnell, dead or alive.

Three days and three nights they searched, without findin' him, and then give it up. On the fourth night my poor Conal returned home, and slept there that night. And early the next mornin' he was out of his bed, heavy-eyed and downhearted. And wanderin' out of his door, he stood in the door of his forge, with arms crossed and shoulders lent against the jamb of the door, lookin' dejectedly at the ground.

When all at once he heard the clatter of a horse again on the road. And liftin' his eyes, and lookin' down the road, what did he behold but the Wee Red Man again comin' up ridin' upon his pony. But Conal saw this mornin' the Wee Red Fellow had two others, one ridin' before him and one behind him—two of the ugliest old hags that had ever hurt the sight of Conal in his life long.

And when the Wee Red Fellow, between the two beauties, drew up at the forge and said, "Good-mornin', Conal O'Donnell," 'tis gruff enough Conal answered, "Good-mornin'."

"Conal O'Donnell," says the Wee Red Man, "would you lend me the loan of your forge fire for a few minutes, this mornin'?"

And Conal, who was always the heart and soul of a good fellow, never could deny nothing to no-body, answered him, "Yes, with a heart and a half, you can have the loan of my forge fire."

And Conal stood aside to see what trick the Wee Red Fellow was up to this mornin'.

The lad jumped off his pony, and takin' hold of the two ugly old hags, in his arms, he lifted them off, and carried them into the forge, and stuck them into the forge fire, and covered them up with coals. And, "Conal O'Donnell," says he, "would you kindly blow the bellows for me?"

Now Conal O'Donnell was all dumbfoundered. But he was too polite to question a stranger. So the bellows he worked like a Connaughtman, and the flames went up like fury. And when at length

Conal O'Donnell considered that the two old hags must be burnt to a cinder, the Little Red Man says, "I think they're done, now."

And goin' to the fire, and rakin' the coals aside, behold ye, the Little Red Fellow lifted out of the fire the most beautiful young maiden that Conal had ever beheld in all his born days—carried her out and saited her on the pony, jumped up behind, and said, "Good-mornin', good luck to ye, and thank ye, Conal O'Donnell!" and rode off.

All dumbfoundered, Conal stood in his forge door, lookin' after the disappearing pair. And when his speeches come to him, says he to himself, "Well, that's the wonderfullest and the convenientest way that I ever heard tell of turnin' ugly old hags into beautiful young maidens. Now," says Conal, says he, "I have an ugly old wife and an ugly old mother-in-law in the house here, and from cock-crow to candlelight the sorra a thing they do but jarrin' and jibin', squabblin' and scoldin', and when the two of them aren't scoldin' one another, both of them are scoldin' me. Now," says he, "wouldn't it be a fine thing entirely if I could only get a beautiful young maiden out of the pair of them."

126

Without any more ado, into the house he went, and there he saw his ugly old wife, at one side of the fire, and his ugly old mother-in-law, on the other side of the fire, and they were jarrin' and squabblin', and scoldin', and both of them spittin' at each other across the fire.

"Well, by this and by that," says Conal, says he, stampin' his foot in the middle of the floor, "but I'll soon and sudden put an end to this!"

And running at them he got hold of the pair in his arms, and carried them out, screamin' and yellin' and howlin' and kickin', and kickin' and kickin'! and stuck the both of them into the forge fire, and covered them up with coals. Then to the bellows he went, and worked like a Connaught-man, and the flames come up like furies, around the old women. And when at length Conal considered that they were done, he went to the fire, brushed the coals aside, and, lo and behold ye, they were both done—brown—burnt to two cinders in the fire.

Poor Conal threw up his hands, shoutin', "Now my life is lost, entirely. The King of Ireland'll behead me for killin' his horse, and, after, they'll hang me for murderin' my wife and my mother-in-law!"

Out of the back window he jumped, and away to the woods. He ran three days and three nights, without stoppin', and on the fourth day, tired and hungry, he sat down beside a stream of water and took out of his pocket the last bit of bread he had in the world to eat.

But just that instant Conal heard a piteous voice at his elbow say, "Conal O'Donnell, I'm very hungry. Will you divide with me?" And lookin' around, who should he see, at his shoulder, but the Wee Red Man.

Little as was the love that Conal owed the Little Red Man, the moment he saw the hungry look in the little fellow's eyes, Conal broke his bread in two, and gave half of it to his enemy.

The Wee Red Fellow clapped his hands, sayin', "Why, Conal O'Donnell, you're the best-hearted man in all the world, and I'd like to help you."

"Help me," says Conal, "help me. You have helped me, sure enough, and 'tis no more of your kind of help I'm hungerin' for. Begone from my sight!"

"Oh, but Conal," says the Little Red Fellow, "I'm goin' to help you now in real earnest. Wherever you go I'll go with you as your servant-boy. And I assure you, you'll win fame and fortune."

But no, no, no, Conal protested that he wouldn't have the Wee Red Fellow around him, if he was paved with golden guineas from the crown of his head to the sole of his foot. But 'twas all no use; the Little Red Fellow insisted and persisted so, that Conal at length, in order to get rid of him, had to let him come with him.

Off, then, they started upon their travels, and at a point where the road was crossin' a high hill, they saw a post standin' up with a placard on it. And when they read it, what the placard said was that the King of France was dyin', and all the greatest doctors in the world had tried to cure him, but had failed. And the Queen of France was now offerin' five bags of gold to any doctor in all the world who would cure the King.

The Little Red Man he shouted for joy. "Now, Conal," says he, "your fortune is made. It's go to France you'll do, and cure the King, and get five bags of gold."

"Is it me," says Conal, says he, "to cure the

King? Why, I couldn't cure a calf, let alone a king.

"Oh, but," says the Little Red Man, "when I'm with you, there's nothin' in the world we can't do."

And the Little Red Fellow wouldn't give Conal either aise or peace till he consented to go. And he was so insistent that he pushed Conal before him till they came to France, and came to the King of France's castle. There the Wee Red Man knocked on the gates of the castle, and a soldier comin' out asked them who they were, and what they wanted.

Says the Wee Red Man, "This is my master, Conal O'Donnell, the most famious doctor in all Ireland, come here to cure your King."

And when the soldier took a look at the famous doctor, he drew his sword, and with the flat of the sword began wallopin' both of them away.

But that instant there was a window thrown up in the castle, and who but the Queen herself, stuck her head out of the window, and called to the soldier what it was he was drivin' these two people away for?

Says the soldier, lookin' up at her, "These two

ragged impostures would pretend that one of them is a famous doctor, come to cure the King.

"Oh, don't drive them away, don't drive them away," says she. "When all the greatest doctors in the world have tried to cure him, and have failed, they can't anyhow do worse than the greatest doctor of them all. Bring them in," says she, "and let them have a try, anyhow."

And the soldier led the two of them into the castle, and up to the King's bedchamber. There was the King lying there, a horrid sight. All the greatest doctors in the world had tried their hand on him, and he was only worse after every doctor; and now he was given up and was dying entirely. The Queen and all the court filled the room, cryin' over him, trying to keep up his heart while he was dyin'.

When the soldier pushed the two lads into the chamber, the Queen, with clasped hands, ran toward them.

"Oh," says she, "do you think you can cure my King for me?"

The Wee Red Man stepped between her and Conal, saying, "Yes, madam, my master he thinks little about curin' a dozen Kings before breakfast-time."

She asked him what necessities his master required to help him cure the King, and the Wee Red Man ordered first a pot of boiling water be brought in and hung on the fire in the bedchamber —which was instantly done. Then he said his master was shy about curin' Kings when people were around; they must all leave the room. The Queen and all the court trooped out of the room, while the Little Red Man closed the door, and turned the key in it.

When Conal found himself and the Little Red Man left alone with the dying King, he began to shake and to shiver, and, "What-what-what is it you're up to now?" says Conal, says he.

Says the Little Red Man, "You hold your tongue, and do as I tell ye. Look around ye, Conal, and get me a carvin' knife."

The two hands of Conal went up in the air, as he shouted, "No, no, no! No more of your carvin' knives for me!"

But the Little Red Man commanded Conal so that he had to obey. And Conal had to search, and find, and carry in the carvin' knife, that was

droppin' out of his shakin' fingers, as he fetched it
to him. Then the Little Red Man stooped down
to the hearthstone, and sharpened up the carvin'
knife, and sharpened it up, and sharpened it up,
till the edge of it could only be fingered very
jinteely.

Then, while Conal was lookin' on, shakin' and
shiverin' with his two knees knockin' together, the
Little Red Man went over to the bed, where the
King was lyin' dying, took hold of the King by
the hair of the head, and cut the head off him. He
carried it over and put it in the kettle of boilin'
water on the fire.

"Now, Conal," says he, "look about ye and get a
stick and stir the King's head in the pot."

But Conal had collapsed in a chair.

"No, no," he groaned. "I'll have no hand in
this murder."

"Hold your tongue," says the Little Red Man,
"and do as I tell ye!" And Conal, behold ye, had
to get hold of a stick, and begin stirrin' the King's
head in the pot. And as he stirred, and stirred,
and stirred, the head melted and melted and
melted, till at length it melted away complete!

Then Conal collapsed. "And now," says he, "our lives are lost, anyhow!"

"Hold your tongue," says the Little Red Fellow, says he, "and get up and go on stirring the pot!"

And Conal had to begin again stirrin' away and stirrin' away, and, behold ye, he hadn't been another minute stirrin' when he beheld a new little head beginnin' to come in the pot. And as he stirred away and stirred away, the head grew away and grew away, till at length it was the full size. And then the Little Red Fellow, comin' over, and lookin' in, said, "I think it's done, now."

He lifted the head out of the pot, and stuck the head on the King, in the bed. And that instant the King sat up in his bed, and began talkin', and chattin', and laughin', completely cured, better than ever he'd been in all his born days.

Then when the Little Red Fellow let in the Queen and the court, and they beheld the King sittin' up in bed, talkin', chattin', and laughin', completely cured, the Queen, with screams of joy, first embraced and kissed the King. And with her arms wide, she ran at Conal.

"No, ma'am, thank you," says Conal, says he,

raisin' his hand against her. "I've a wife of me own at home."

On her knees then she fell with hands clasped, to thank Conal from the bottom of her heart. "You're surely," says she, "the most famous doctor the world ever knew. "And," says she, "I'll give you your weight in gold every year, if you remain and be the King's doctor for the remainder of your days."

"No, ma'am," says Conal, says he. "The people at home in Ireland will be dyin', and I must hurry home to cure them. Get me up my five bags of gold."

The Queen had the butler get up the five bags of gold out of the cellar. And the Little Red Fellow got the bags on his back, and off for Ireland both of them set.

When they had traveled three days and three nights, the Little Red Fellow looked down at his shoes, saw that they were badly worn, with his ten toes stickin' out through them.

And, "Conal," says he, "will you buy me a new pair of shoes?"

Now when Conal was a poor man, he was, as you remimber, the best-hearted man in all the world, would divide his last bit of bread with his enemy. But now that he was a rich man, his nature was completely changed. And he answered back the Little Red Fellow: "No, the times is hard, and money scarce, and I can't afford you any shoes. The ones you have will do you well enough. Go on and carry home my gold to Ireland."

And the instant he showed himself a bad fellow the Little Red Man, with the five bags of gold upon his back, rose up into the air, and disappeared through the skies, leavin' Conal upon the road, alone and lonely, poorer than he had ever been in all his life afore!

Conal's heart sank into his shoes, and he went stumblin' along the road, wonderin' what he'd do, at all, at all. Next minute his hangin' head struck again' somethin', and, behold ye, it was a post on the roadside, and there was a placard on the post. And Conal looked up to see what it was the placard said.

And, behold ye, what it said was that the King of Spain was dying. All the greatest doctors in the world had tried to cure him, but they had all failed, and the Queen was now offering ten bags of gold to any doctor in all the world who could cure the King.

For joy, Conal clapped his hands, and said, "Now my fortune's made, for now I know how to cure Kings." And off he started runnin', and never stopped till he was in Spain, and at the King's castle, and rattling on the gate.

And when he told the soldier who came out, that he was the famous Irish doctor, Conal O'Donnell, the soldier cried out: "Why, we've been searchin' all the world for you. The Queen heard how you cured the King of France, and was screengin' the earth's corners to get you. Come in, come in!" And he led Conal up to the King's bedchamber, where the Queen and all the court filled the room. And the King, given up by all the greatest doctors, was dyin' entirely.

When the soldier led Conal in, and announced that he was the famous Irish doctor, Conal O'Donnell, come to cure the King, the Queen almost fainted for joy, and threw herself on her knees before Conal, and begged, "Oh, great Irish doctor, do you think you can cure my King for me?"

"Ma'am," says Conal, says he, "I'll make short work of your man for you."

She then asked him what he required to help cure the King. And what he wanted was a pot of boiling water to be hung upon the fire, and then all people to leave the room. Both of these things were soon done, and he had the door locked behind them.

Then, when he was left alone with the dying King, the first thing he did, naturally, was to look for a carvin' knife. And then, stooping down by the hearthstone, he sharpened up the carvin' knife, and sharpened it up, and sharpened it up, till he had a fine jinteel point upon the carvin' knife. And then, taking the dying King by the hair o' the head, he cut the head off the King, and dropped the head into the pot of boiling water on the fire, and getting a stick, began stirrin' the King's head in the pot. As he stirred away and stirred away, the head melted away and melted away, until at length the head completely disappeared.

"It's doin' fine," says Conal. "It's half done now."

And then he went on stirrin' away and watchin' away, and stirrin' away and watchin' away, but, behold ye, if he had been stirrin' away and watchin' away from that day to this, he couldn't get any new head to come in the pot.

And after an hour of this the Queen and the court began beatin' at the doors, to get in, and there was the King lyin' on the bed, without a head to him!

Conal, he collapsed on the floor, cryin', "Now, my life is done, anyhow, and right well I do deserve it."

Just at that very instant wasn't there a tip-tap-tipping at the window. And lookin' over, who should he see but the Little Red Man perched on the window-sill wantin' to get in.

In three shakes of a lamb's lug, Conal had the window thrown up, and the Little Red Man had hopped into the room. And snatchin' the stick from Conal's hand, he began stirrin' the pot.

And, behold ye, he hadn't given three stirs to the pot when Conal looked in and saw a new little head begin to come in the pot! And three stirs more, and, behold ye, the head was the full size! Then the Little Red Man looked in and said, "I think it's done now."

And taking the head from the pot, he went over and stuck the head on the King in the bed, and that instant the King sat up, and began chattin' and talkin' and laughin', completely cured, better than ever he'd been in all of his born days. Then the Wee Red Fellow said, "Conal, I'll wait for you outside," and hopped out of the window.

When Conal opened the door, and the Queen and the court came in, and saw the King sittin' up, and talkin' and chattin' and laughin' in bed, the Queen, overcome with joy, embraced and kissed the King, and then fell on her knees before Conal, thankin' him from the bottom of her heart, and offerin' him three times his weight in gold, as a salary every year, if he'd remain and be the King's doctor for the remainder of his life.

But Conal said, "No, ma'am. The people in Ireland will be dyin' and I must hurry home to cure them. Get me up my ten bags of gold, as quickly as you can."

For Conal was tremblin' in his skin for fear that the King should take it in his mind to sneeze, and the head of him come bouncin' on the floor again, before he got paid.

When he went out, the Little Red Man got the ten bags of gold upon his back, and off they started home for Ireland. Three days and three nights they traveled before them, and on the fourth day the Little Red Man looked down at his shoes, saw that they were badly worn, with his ten toes stickin' out through them, and he said, "Conal, buy me a new pair of shoes."

Says Conal, says he, "Go buy yourself a hundred thousand pairs of shoes. The money is yours, and not mine. It is you that have earned it, and it is you that has the right to spend it all for whatsoever you please."

"Why, Conal," says the Wee Red Man, "you are your own good-hearted self again. "Now," says he, "I want no shoes from you; I want none of your gold. I want nothing, for I'm one of the gentle people, the fairies, and anything in the world I want, I've only to wish for, and I'll have it. I only asked you that to test you. Now that you're your own good-hearted self, the gold is yours, and I'll carry it home for you to Ireland."

And off they started, and never stopped, halted, nor paused, till they reached Ireland, and reached the top of the hill above Conal's own house, where they could see Conal's house and forge lying in the valley below.

There the Little Red Man laid down the ten

bags of gold to Conal, and he said, "Now, Conal, you're the wealthiest, and happiest man in all Ireland. Good-by, good-luck to you, and God bless you!" And rising up in the air, he disappeared through the skies.

Conal looked at his ten bags of gold, and said: "Now I'm the wealthiest man in all Ireland, and I'm the happiest— Oh, no," says he, as old memories flashed on him, "I'm not happy! Sure the King of Ireland will behead me for killin' his horse, and after that they'll hang me for murderin' my wife and my mother-in-law. Sure," says he, "instead of being the happiest, it's the miserablest divil I am, in all Ireland."

And a doleful eye he cast down to his house, in the valley below. And there, behold ye, first thing he saw was the King of Ireland's beautiful dancin', prancin', yellow steed, standin' up outside his forge, with a new set of legs under him, and a new set of shoes to them. And the next thing he beheld was his wife and his mother-in-law alive and well, comin' runnin' out of the house to greet him. With a joyful cry, he hoisted the ten bags of gold on his back, and went galloping down the hillside.

And, behold ye, when he met his wife and his

mother-in-law, he found that they were not only alive and well, but both of them had grown young and beautiful—and, what is more than all else besides, both of them were grown good-tempered once again.

Conal, all rejoiced, went home with his arms around them, and next day, in his joy, he married his wife again. And he asked all the worl' to the weddin'. And that was the greatest weddin' ever known before or since. It lasted nine days and nine nights, and the last day and night was better than the first. And Conal built a castle with a window for every day in the year, where he and his wife, and his mother-in-law lived happy and well, ever after.

THE QUEEN OF THE LONELY ISLE

ONCE upon a time the King of Donegal was in the south of Ireland hunting, for he was a very great sportsman indeed. And on a day he started a fox which left all the hounds behind, and all the hunters, too, except only the King. My brave King stuck to the fox over hill and vale and long green plain, till at last, late in the evening, the fox reached the River Shannon, plunged in and swam out of sight toward the mouth of the river—and was lost to the King.

Next day the King set out for the hunt again, and at the selfsame spot, started the same fox. The fox flew at such a rate that it outdistanced all the dogs and left all the hunters behind—except only the King, who stuck close by the fox over hill and vale, and long green plain, till in the evening late, when they reached the River Shannon, the fox took to the water, and passed away out of the

King's sight. When the King got home that night, he swore that if he started that fox again he would never stop till he had killed it.

And the next day, when the King and his party went out, the same fox was started from the same spot. But this day the King's hound almost caught her—he had her by the heel before she had well started—but the fox freed herself and again outdistanced all the dogs; and left far behind all the hunters—except the King, who this time, stuck still closer and closer by her, over hill and vale, and long green plain, till late in the evening they reached the River Shannon. The fox took to the river, swimming toward its mouth, but the King plunged in his horse after, and fast as the fox swam, the King's horse didn't swim any less fast.

Till at long and at last the fox reached an island far out at sea, and ran inland on the island. The King reached it and galloped inland also, tracing the animal by a trail of blood from its wounded heel. At length the trail took him to a little hut— the only sign of habitation he had seen on this lonely isle. At the hut he lost trace of the fox.

The King said, "I'll go into this hut and inquire."

He was surprised to see an old woman sitting by the fireside, washing a wounded, bleeding heel. Feeling great pity for the poor woman, the King knelt down and washed and dressed her wound. And the foot, which looked to be a rough and common foot, when he first began dressing it, became the most beautiful foot he had ever seen, before he was finished. And when he rose, behold! he found himself not in a little hut, but in a dazzling hall of a most magnificent castle. And instead of an old woman, he found he had dressed the foot of the most beautiful damsel his eye had ever beheld.

"What's the meaning of all this?" said the King.

Said the damsel: "I'm the Queen of the Isle of Loneliness, and sometimes long to see something of the world. But I cannot visit it in my own shape; so by my magical power I turn myself into a fox. I was the fox whom you hunted, and the old woman whose wounded foot you pitied and dressed. I didn't intend to let you know me in reality, but since you showed such fine feeling for one whom you believed to be an old woman, I could not help letting you know the truth. Myself and my court," she said, "make you welcome to remain as long as you like in the Isle of Loneliness."

The King, enchanted with the damsel, and with everything he saw, agreed to remain for a day. But the day grew to a week, and the week to a month and he was still more enchanted with the damsel, and wooing her eagerly. Till at length, when he had wooed her without ceasing for three months, she consented to marry him.

And when he was married to the Queen of the Lonely Isle, his days were happy, each succeeding day happier even than the one before; and he neither thought of his kingdom nor of his people for six months.

At the end of that time he remembered his duty, and begged of his Queen to let him go back to Ireland and Donegal, till he would settle the affairs of his kingdom, and leave a new King to reign in his stead. Then he would return to the Isle of Loneliness and never be parted from his Queen again.

She begged him not to leave her. But so much did he grieve for his people without a King, that at length, to satisfy and make him happy, she consented to let him go. She mounted him on a magic white steed, which could go over water as easily as over land; and she warned him, on leaving, not to let living being touch his lips till he returned. For, she said, if his lips were touched by living being, he would forget all about her and the Isle of Loneliness.

He gave the promise, and rode away. And when, after riding long, and long, and far and far, he reached the banks of the Shannon at the same place that he had left it long months ago, he found his hunting party, who had traced him so far on the third day of the hunt, and had been waiting there ever since for his return. Woe-begone they were, and hungry as well, after this long watch; but now that he was come, they all rejoiced. Many of them ran to kiss him; but remembering his wife's warning, he gently pushed them off. At length, however, his favorite dog jumped up, put his paws on his master's shoulders, and kissed his lips.

That instant all memory of his Queen and his life in the Isle of Loneliness went from him. And joyfully, with his friends, he rode back to Donegal, to resume his reign over the people, who had been lamenting his loss.

For years after, his people, who wanted an heir to the throne, wished him to marry, but he, without being able to give a reason to them or to himself, refused. There was in Donegal a handsome Princess, who was anxious to marry the King and be Queen of Donegal. She tried every plan she could think of to make the King take her in marriage. But the King wouldn't think of any woman. Then she began to incense the people against the King, because he would not marry. And she thought that if the King was dethroned, she would be chosen Queen in his stead. At length she found three fearsome Giants in the Islands of Scotland, who were willing, for pay, to come against the King of Donegal, and to kill him and make her Queen. And with these men she bargained.

Now, in less than six months after the King had left the Isle of Loneliness, his Queen gave birth to a son. And when this son grew up, his mother, on his eighteenth birthday, said to him, "Your father, the King of Donegal, in Ireland, who left the Isle of Loneliness before you were born, and has lost all memory of it and of me, is now in great danger. Would you risk your life to save him?"

And the young Prince said, "Surely, I would gladly risk my life to save my father's."

Then she told him that three of the most terrible Giants in the world had come from the Isles of Scotland, and were challenging the King's champions to give up their lives or the King's.

She took from her walls a sword which she buckled on her son, telling him that it was the Sword of Victory. "With this Sword," she said, "you will be invincible. Go and save your father, and when you have saved him, tell him who you are, and maybe he'll remember."

She led him into the castle garden, and, plucking a sunflower, tossed it into the air, when it became a yellow balloon. Into this balloon she put her son, and blew three times on it—when the balloon immediately sailed away, over land and sea, and alighted with the Prince close to the castle of the King of Donegal.

When the Prince reached the castle, he found himself only in the nick of time to save the King's life. Every champion who had gone out against the Giants to fight for their King had thrown away his life. For no one of them could stand for a moment against the smallest of the Giants. Nine champions already had been killed, and all others were afraid to go out.

The young Prince then stepped out, facing first the smallest Giant.

The Giant laughed when he saw this lad of eighteen come against him. He put his finger to the lad, and with one push, pushed him away a mile, saying, "I scorn to kill children!"

The Prince immediately drew his Sword and crying, "Sword be at him!" flew back at the Giant, with such fury that the Giant had to fight.

And a terrible fight it was—the fiercest ever beheld in Donegal. But at length the Prince, giving a bound into the air, ran the Sword of Victory through the Giant and killed him.

Then he went against the second Giant, who laughed at the lad of eighteen, and, putting his finger to him, pushed him away three miles. But the Prince, drawing his Sword, ran back at the Giant; and as he came up, he said, "Sword, be at him!" He attacked the Giant with such fury that the Giant had to fight. And the fight was a hard and terrible one—the fiercest ever beheld in Donegal. But at length the Prince, giving a bound into the air, ran the Sword of Victory through the Giant and killed him.

Then he went to fight the third Giant, who laughed at the lad, and, putting his finger to him, pushed him seven miles. But the young Prince ran back at the Giant, drawing his Sword of Victory and crying, "Sword be at him!" He attacked the Giant with such fury that the Giant had to fight. And a hard and a terrible fight it was—the fiercest ever beheld in Donegal. But at length the young Prince, giving a bound into the air, ran the Sword of Victory through the Giant and killed him.

Great was the rejoicing then. The King led up the young Prince and placed him on a throne at his side, and asked him who he was, and where he came from.

He answered, "I have come from the Island of Loneliness, to save my father's life. My mother is the Queen of the Lonely Isle, and my father is the King of Donegal."

"That's false," said the King. "I never heard of the Lonely Isle, nor of its Queen."

And the boy tried his best to make the King remember, but the King couldn't remember, and said that the young warrior had got crazed by the fight. Still the boy persisted.

The bad Princess, fearing that there might be truth in it, and that the King would yet remember, worked upon the King's feelings, wanting to have the boy killed—to which the King would not consent. But he did give consent to have the boy cast adrift on the ocean.

Far from land the young Prince was taken, and cast adrift in a boat, without food or drink. His mother, seeing from the Island of Loneliness what was happening, took a reel of purple ribbon, and threw it over the waters, till it alighted in her son's boat. She held one end of the ribbon, and then drew it to her till his boat was brought safely back to the Island of Loneliness.

A year and a day later, the Queen called the young prince to her and said, "Today your father is in great peril. The Princess who is working against him has brought three fleets of ships from the Islands of Scotland to attack him in his castle, and kill him, that she may reign in his stead. Would you again risk your life for your father?"

And the young Prince said, "With pleasure would I again risk my life for my father."

She took the Prince with her down to the sea-side, and, plucking a lily that grew by the sea-wall, threw it on the waters, where immediately it was a beautiful little ship, full-rigged, and manned by little men. Three stones from her pocket she took and gave to the Prince, and said, "Get into that boat, and go to the harbor by the castle of your father, where the three fleets are getting ready to attack him. Into each fleet, throw one of these stones, and your father's life will be saved."

The Prince got aboard the boat, which immediately started over the waters with the speed of the sunlight, and in a short time sailed into the harbor by the castle of his father.

There he saw three fleets from the Scottish Isles getting ready to attack his father in his castle, and he went out with his little boat against the three fleets. And the captains of the fleets, when they saw him come, laughed heartily at the crazy little fellow, as they called him. Up to one fleet he sailed, and threw a stone into it, when immediately the whole fleet went afire. Then the second fleet he charged, and threw a stone into the center of it—which went afire also. Then the third fleet he charged, and threw a stone into the center of it.

And that instant the third fleet was afire. And quickly all three fleets were burnt upon the waters.

The King and his people went down to the sea, and there was great rejoicing. Since the Prince had gone away, the King, who had loved him from the first and who had consented against his will to send him away, had deeply grieved. He now received the young Prince with the greatest delight, asked him where he had been, and where he now came from.

The young Prince said, "I have been at home in the Isle of Loneliness, with the Queen, my mother, who today sent me here to save the life of my father, the King of Donegal."

The King was sorry to hear him say this, and said, "The poor boy is crazed by the battle."

But the boy persisted in saying that the King was his mother's husband.

The bad Princess worked upon the King and the people to consent, though they would not directly take the boy's blood on their hands, to let him walk blindfolded over a precipice to his death.

When the day for his death had come, and the boy, blindfolded, was sent to walk over the terrible precipice, behold you! his mother, the Queen, who knew from the Isle of Loneliness what was happening, threw from her to the cliff over which he was about to walk, a golden clew—and immediately there was a bridge of gold from the cliff to the Isle of Loneliness, thousands of miles away. And over the bridge of gold the Prince passed to his home.

A year and a day after that the Queen of the Isle of Loneliness called her son, and said, "Your father is about to lose his life this day. Are you willing to risk your life for his?"

Said the young prince: "With pleasure would I risk my life to save my father's."

Then she said, "Because your father still refuses to marry, the Princess who has twice before tried to·have him killed has now succeeded in stirring up his people against him. He is a prisoner in his castle, and in short time he is to be led out before the castle wall, where a hundred of the best marksmen in Donegal are to shoot him dead with their arrows. You must instantly go to save him."

She led the young Prince to the castle gate, and striking the gate with her wand, a winged horse appeared. She breathed three times on her son, saying, "That's the breath of God's blessing; you have now nothing to fear, and naught can harm you. Ride to your father's castle on this winged horse, stand before him when the arrows are let fly, and save his life."

The young Prince mounted the winged horse, and off through the air sped like the lightning, and he alighted at his father's castle just as his father was led out and stood up against the castle wall, with a hundred of the best marksmen in Donegal drawn up before him, a hundred yards away.

But as the Princess, whom the people were now about to make Queen, gave the marksmen the command to bend their bows and shoot, the Prince sprang in front of his father, and throwing out his arms he gathered to his own breast the hundred arrows that filled the air. And instantly he held an armful of fragrant lilies.

With a great shout of surprise all the people rushed forward. And the King sprang to the Prince, took him in his arms and kissed him.

The moment that the King's lips touched his son's the memory of all forgotten things rushed upon him. He recalled the Isle of Loneliness and its beautiful Queen, his wife. Then he proclaimed to the people that he was indeed married, and to the most beautiful Queen in all the world, and that this was his son who had three times saved his life. He told them of his adventure, and of how he had lost his memory through letting the dog kiss him.

He gave them his son to be King of Donegal. And he went to the Isle of Loneliness and brought his Queen from there for the son's crowning. There was never such joy and delight in any kingdom, as was that day in Donegal, for they were to crown the bravest young hero that the world had ever known.

And if that day was joyous for the people of Donegal, it was not one bit less joyous for the King and Queen and their brave son. And happy as that day was, each following day of their lives was happier still.

THE STEED O' BELLS

ONCE upon a time when pigs were swine, when pigeons built their nests in old men's beards, and turkeys chewed tobacco, there was a King and Queen who had three sons, and the Queen died and the King married again, and the stepmother hated the three young Princes, was very bad to them, and strove all she could to get them put away. But the King, though he liked her very much and would humor her in everything else, would never consent to give in to her on this point: and no matter what she did or what she tried it was all no use—she couldn't persuade the King to an agreement with her.

There was an old hen-wife living near the castle, and the Queen went to consult her regarding how she should get rid of her three stepsons.

The hen-wife said she would manage it for her if she was well paid.

"What payment do you want?" says the Queen.

"Three things," says the old hen-wife. "As much meal as will make my breakfast, as much milk as will sup it, and as much wool as will stuff my ears."

The Queen said she would readily agree to that.

And then the hen-wife told her to invite her stepsons to play a game of cards, and when they would ask what they would play for she would say for *geasa* (obligations). She said, "If they win they will lay something trifling on you; but if you win, which is most likely, you lay *geasa* upon them to steal for you the Knight of the Glen's Steed of Bells, which three hundred champions have gone to steal before, and every one of them lost their lives."

The Queen was pleased at this, and said she would send the hen-wife her pay, but she asked the hen-wife how much meal would make her breakfast. And she said all the grinding of seven times seven mills for seven years. How much milk would sup it? She said the yield of the cows of seven times seven hills for seven years. And

how much wool would stuff her ears? The produce of the sheep of seven times seven plains for
seven years. And as the Queen had bargained so,
there was no way out of it but to pay her hire.

The Queen went home, and invited her stepsons
to play her a game of cards. They agreed, and
asked her what they should play for.

"For *geasa*," said she.

Well and good; down to the card-table they
sat, and when they had finished she had won two
games off the two oldest, but had lost the game
to the youngest. These two demanded to know
their *geasa*, and she said that they were to set out
on the morrow and never come home till they
brought with them to her the Knight of the Glen's
Steed of Bells that three hundred champions had
gone before to steal, and none ever come back
alive.

The youngest was sad and sorry when he heard
such *geasa* put upon his brothers. And he said,
"If my brothers go I will not stay behind; I will
go with them." And says he, "The *geasa* I will
leave upon you is that you stand on the top of my
father's tower with your face to the wind, and
for food and drink a sheaf of corn and a tub of

water; and there remain till we come back with the Knight of the Glen's Steed of Bells."

And this she had to do.

They set off, and when they had been traveling three days and three nights they met a man on horseback who asked them where they were going, and what errand they were on. They told him where they were going and what was their errand.

"Oh, well, well!" says he. "I tell you three hundred champions have tried that before, and every one of them lost his life. I am the famous Black Thief of Sloan; I myself tried to steal the Steed of Bells three times, and the most my cleverness got for me was to bring me off with my life again. The Knight of the Glen has an army of men guarding his Steed of Bells by day and by night, and, moreover, every time a thief would lay his hands upon the horse, the horse gives himself one shake and the sound of his bells is heard over half the world."

"Well," they said, "all we can do is make the best of a bad matter, and the worst that can come upon us is to lose our lives; and we are prepared for that."

"You're brave, bold fellows," said the Thief, "and I admire you, and if you are bent on trying, why, I will go with you and give you any help I can, and at the worst lose my life along with you."

They were very, very thankful to the Black Thief of Sloan, so they joined with him, and all four journeyed far and far before them, till they came to the castle of the Knight of the Glen.

The Black Thief of Sloan said the luck was in their favor, for there was a great feast in the castle that night, and every one was drinking and carousing. The Black Thief very easily stole a keg of wine, and rolled it out of the castle yard among the guards who stood upon the stables. They fell to drinking the wine, and before midnight they were all lying asleep.

"Now is our chance," said the Black Thief; "we'll try."

Into the stable they went, and the moment they touched the Steed he shook himself, and the sound of the bells was heard over half the world.

The Knight was roused inside, and called on his men to rush to the stables, for there was a thief in them. The Black Thief hid himself and the three brothers in a loft. The men came in and examined the stables, went back and reported to the Knight that there was no thief.

The second time they laid hands on the horse, and the second time he shook his bells. And the Knight ordered his men to see if there was a thief in it this time. The Thief hid himself and the brothers so that the men returned to the Knight and reported that there was no thief. Then a third time they tried the Steed of Bells, and the third time the Steed sounded the alarm.

The Knight said, "There is surely a thief in the stable. Come, I will go with you and search myself."

And the Knight searched so thoroughly that he discovered all four of them. He made his soldiers march them into the hall. He had a big caldron brought in from the courtyard, put on the fire and filled with oil; for the sentence upon any one who attempted to steal the Knight of the Glen's Steed of Bells was that he should be boiled in this caldron of oil.

The Knight said to the Black Thief that three times before he had attempted to steal his Steed, and three times he had escaped. "But now," he says, "your minute is come. You will be the first man boiled in the caldron. How does it feel," says the Knight, "to know you are so near your death?"

But the Black Thief made light of it.

"Oh," said he, "I have been as near death before and escaped, and maybe I will escape this time too."

"Hardly," says the Knight. "But," says the Knight, "before we put you into the caldron you might prove to us you were as near death before and escaped."

"I will do that," says the Thief, "if you will pardon the youngest of the brothers on condition that my story shows I was as near death before."

"I will do that," says the Knight.

"Well, there was once," says the Thief, "when I went to rob a gentleman's castle. I had my face blackened all over, and when I came to the castle in the middle of the night I found it all lit up and the place in a great furore. It seems that robbers had been there not an hour before and had robbed the castle, and alarmed it, and gone off, and the gentleman's servants and soldiers were scouring the country to find them. If they found

165

me I knew they would have my life on the spot, so I took to my heels in a great fright and didn't stop running for nine miles. Then I drew on a house with a fire lit in it, but nobody to be seen without or within, and I went in and was warming myself in the kitchen when I heard voices and the tramp of people coming up to the door. I said to myself it was the gentlemen's servants still pursuing the robbers, and that I was caught.

"Without any delay I jumped on the half loft overhead, and lay among sheepskins and horses' harness that were there. I wasn't right up when in at the door comes three men, who were no other than the three robbers that had robbed the castle, and they dragging the boxes of gold and silver with them.

"They sat down at the fire, and began to count the money. They were saying to one another how well it was for them that they happened to reach the castle before the Black Thief of Sloan. From what they had heard I was going to rob the castle that night, and that was why they went earlier to get all the wealth before I did. They said I had been too long robbing the country, and my clev-

erness was such that no other honest robber got
a chance, and all the robbers of the country, in-
cluding themselves, were sworn in conspiracy to
have my life and put me out of the way.

"As ill luck would have it, I gave a sneeze
above their heads, and all three of them that moment jumped to their feet and drew their knives.
For poor me, I had neither knife nor else on or
about me, for in my race for safety I had thrown
everything away.

"They said, 'Some one is over our heads watching all we're doing and listening to all we're saying. We can never let him go out of this house
alive.'

"There was one big black fellow of them who
said it was better not to kill him yet awhile, but
leave him there till they would have the pot
boiled, and then they could kill half the life of
him and boil out the other half. All of them at
once agreed to this. So the black fellow put on
the pot and the three of them began to sharpen
the knives.

"Myself was lying on a loose plank above, and
all at once I was seized with a terrible fit of trembling. I trembled and shook so much that the

plank very soon gave way, and down into the middle of them I tumbled, with the harness chains rattling after me. My face was black, and a ram's skin on top of me with the horns resting right on my head.

" 'It's the devil! It's the devil! It's the devil!' all three of them shouted at once, and took to their heels yelling and screeching; and flew out, one of them at the front door, another at the back door, another clean through the window, and left me in possession of all the gold and silver.

"And don't you think," says the Black Thief to the Knight of the Glen, "that I was as near death then as I am now and escaped?"

"I agree," says the Knight of the Glen, "that you were, and I give the youngest his life."

"And for all that," says the Black Thief, "there was another time when death was as near me as either that time or this time."

"Will you tell us that and let us judge for ourselves before we put you in the caldron?" says the Knight.

"I will," says the Black Thief, "on condition that you pardon the second brother."

And the Knight of the Glen said he would agree

to that, if this escape was as narrow and as wonderful.

"Well," said the Black Thief of Sloan, "there were, one time, three witches in Scotland, who were known to all the robbers of the world as having immense wealth; but no robber had ever been able to rob them—only lost his life in the attempt.

"I determined that I would try. I set out to Scotland and came to their place, and went into the house in the middle of the night when I knew they were asleep. And I found them sleeping with their bags of gold under their heads for pillows. I got three pillow-slips and went and filled them with shingles and took them in, and as I worked the bag of gold from under each witch's head I was working the bag of shingles under her head instead. I got the three bags safe with me and away. But, behold you, I hadn't put three hills behind me when I saw the three witches coming in hot pursuit in the shape of three hounds, and I believed my life was as good as done for. I dropped the three bags of gold and ran for all I was worth. Fast and fast as I ran, they were gaining ground on me very quickly, and they got that near me that I almost felt their breath.

"I rushed up an ash tree, and when they reached the bottom of it one of them turned into a hatchet and one of them into a saw, and began chopping and sawing the tree at the bottom, and the other turned herself into her own shape, and waited for the tree to fall down, till she would tear me limb from limb. The hatchet and the saw were working faster and faster and nearly meeting through the tree, when at last I found the tree beginning to tremble, and the heart was in my mouth for I felt now it was all over with me.

"But at that very instant the cock crew for break of day, and the witches had to change themselves immediately into their own shape and away with them as fast as ever they could.

"And don't you think, Knight, that that was a narrow escape?"

"It was," said the Knight, "and I pardon the second brother. But I am sure you never had another escape so narrow."

"I had that," says the Black Thief of Sloan, "and I will tell it to you and prove it to you, if you will pardon the third brother."

"Agreed," says the Knight. "I was not so anxious to kill these boys, anyhow; it's yourself I'm most wishful to kill, for while you were alive I was never content and could not think my Steed safe."

"There was once when I was away on a robbing expedition," says the Black Thief of Sloan, "and was traveling through wild and rocky mountains many hundred miles from here, I stumbled over a spink one evening and fell and rolled, and rolled and fell, till I reached the bottom in a narrow gorge with steep sides far below. And what should I find there but a great, big, ugly Giant cooking his supper. He said, 'I'm glad, I'm glad, for I hadn't as much meat here as would take the edge off my appetite.'

"So he went to reach for me, but I took hold of a spit that was lying with its point reddened in the fire and ran his two eyes out with it. He roared that loud that I thought the hills would crack, and he yelled that he would give me the most beautiful death that ever a man got in the world before. He couldn't see anything now, of course, but he came along towards me with his two hands spread out, and the little gorge was that narrow that there was no chance of passing him without his feeling me, though I backed away and away up the gorge before him.

"At the end of the gorge was a cave, and into this cave I went. It was deep and wide and filled with goats, and I said to myself that when he came into the cave to look for me I could very easily escape him and get out. But he was too wise for that. He sat down in the narrow mouth of the cave and slept there all night, and he told me he would never leave that spot till I would come out and he could catch me.

"In the morning he called on his goats to come out. They crept past him one by one, and he caught hold of every one as it passed, putting his arms round its neck, and said, 'Oh, my dear, good goat, you can see me, your master, but I can't see you since the Black Thief put out my eyes. But I'll soon put his life out for it.'

"Now, there was one great big buck-goat in the cave. When I found the goats beginning to go out, I got the big buck by the throat and put his life out. I took his skin and got into it, then went on my hands and knees into the line of goats that were passing out.

"The Giant was embracing every goat as it passed him, and talking to it, and when I came up he got his arms round my neck too, and said, 'Oh, my dear, good old buck, you see me but I can't see you, since the Black Thief put out my eyes, but I will soon put his life out for it.' Then he let me go and got hold of the next goat, and I wasn't long showing a clean pair of heels and getting out of the gorge and free.

"Don't you think, Knight," said he, "that that was as narrow an escape?"

"Yes, it was surely," said the Knight, "and I pardon the third brother. But now you go into the caldron yourself and die."

"I'm not so sure of that," says the Black Thief of Sloan, "for I was nearer death before and escaped."

Says the Knight, "On no account can I think of sparing your life. But all the same," says he, we'll spare it for half an hour to hear the wonderful story."

"Good," says the Black Thief of Sloan. "When I was returning through the same country again where I had the encounter with the Giant, I came late one evening to a castle, and went into it to ask lodgings for the night. I found a girl sitting at the kitchen fire with a baby on her knee, and she crying hard.

"Says I, 'My girl, what's the matter?' And she told me.

" 'In this castle,' she says, 'there lives a Giant who is blind, because his eyes were put out some-how or other. He has compelled me into his ser-vice, and makes me do whatever he wants. This is a little child that he stole from somewhere and brought me last night, and when he was leaving this morning he ordered me to have it cooked for his supper when he would return this night.' She says, 'I can't do it, and when he comes home and finds it not killed or cooked, he will kill me.'

"I says, 'Never mind, I'll fix that.' So I went out to the yard and killed a little pig; I cut off the left-hand little finger of the child and made her cook it with the pig, and when the Giant at length came home and asked for his supper, she gave him the pig in a dish.

"But he wasn't long eating till he got up in a thundering rage and asked her was it the pig she cooked for him instead of the child. She denied it, and she went to the dish and lifted the little

finger of the child and gave it to him as proof—
which contented him and he finished the supper.
Then he said he hadn't half enough and asked for
a knife, saying he must get some more.

I ran away out of his road, and stumbled into
a room where there were a row of dead bodies
freshly killed. But wasn't this the very place the
Giant was coming to! I lay down among the
bodies myself, stiff like the others. He came and
he felt the bodies one after another and threw
them from him, till at last to my great terror he
got hold of myself and he said, 'This corpse feels
all right. I think I should like a bit of it.'

"He lifted up his knife and he took a slice of
flesh off me, and I never had a more terrible time
trying to keep from moving or screeching whilst
he was cutting the flesh off me; but I did succeed.

"When he had finished his supper he lay down
to sleep. But where did he lie only right across
the door of the room in which I was! I was suffering so much from fright that I wouldn't stay
in the house any longer, so when he was asleep I
leaped over him, and made for the door and got
out. But my leap wakened him and he reached

after me, and taking a ring from his finger threw it from him, saying, 'Ring, ring, hold fast.' On the big toe of my right foot the ring fell and there stuck. He called, 'Ring, ring, where are you?' And the ring answered, 'Master, master, I am here.'

"So that no matter whither I ran the ring informed him and kept him on my track. For always he would call, 'Ring, ring, where are you?' and always the ring would answer, 'Master, master, I am here.' And I ran about and dodged about for hours. But though he could not see anything, he always kept close to me, and was still getting closer and closer.

"At length I was passing by a great bottomless pool. I pulled a knife from my pocket, cut off my big toe and threw it with the ring into the heart of the pool; and when next the Giant called, 'Ring, ring, where are you?' and it replied from the bottom of the pool, 'Master, master, I am here', —into the heart of the pool he dashed, and sank and never rose more, and I was safe.

"And now," said the Thief, reaching out a foot from which he had just stripped both shoe and stocking, "you can see that I lack the big toe of my right foot. And did you ever hear a more wonderful or narrower escape than that?"

"A wonderful and a narrow escape it was," says an old woman who was sitting in the corner. "And what is more," says she, "it's true as it's wonderful. For, I am the very girl, and you," says she to the Knight, "were the very child that he saved—and that is the reason of your wanting the little finger of your left hand."

And when the Knight heard this, it was he who was the surprised, and the astonished, and the glad man.

"For all my life," he says, "I was trying to find out the man who had saved my life, and I was giving up the search in vain, for I thought I never could discover him.

"Now, Black Thief of Sloan," says he, "you will never leave my castle more. You must live with me from this time, and you will never want for anything that's in my power to give. For your friends here, they can not only have their freedom, but what is more, I freely bestow on them my Steed of Bells."

And the Knight and his friends and the Black Thief saw them safely off on their way, the Steed with them; and they thanked the Knight, and they told the Black Thief they could never thank him enough.

They traveled on and on before them till at last they came in sight of their father's castle. Away on the tip-top of it they saw their bad step-mother standing with her face against the wind, a sheaf of corn on the one side of her, and a tub of water on the other, and she thin and woe-begone, and the instant she saw them she dashed herself from the tower and broke her neck below.

Home they reached, and it's glad their father the King was to see them. He divided his king-dom into three parts and gave a part to each, and got them three of the most beautiful Princesses in marriage.

And happy men and women they were, and happy and prosperous were their kingdoms all their days.

THE CU-BEAG* OF THE WILLOW-WOOD

ONCE upon a time, and a good time it was, there were a King and a Queen in Donegal, who had one son called Cormac. A fine, brave, likely boy he was; and when he found himself getting to be a young man, Cormac asked his father's and mother's blessing, saying he would go off to push his fortune. His mother baked him a cake, and asked Cormac whether he would rather have half the cake with her blessing, or the whole of the cake without; and Cormac, with no hesitation, said, "Half the cake, dear Mother, and your blessing." He got half the cake—and his father's and mother's hearty blessing. And, bidding good-by to his friends—who were right sorry to lose him, because Cormac had always been a first favorite —off he set.

* *Cu-beag* is Irish for Little Hound.

At noon-day, hungry and tired, Cormac sat down to eat his cake. Up to him, out of the willow-wood near by, came trotting a little brown dog, with a very hungry look in his eyes. And the dog said, "Cormac, my poor pups haven't tasted food for twenty-four hours—won't you divide your cake with them?"

"Indeed, and I will that," said Cormac, right heartily. For a kindly soul he was, to bird, beast, and fish. So he broke his cake in two, and gave by far the bigger half to the little brown dog.

Then the little brown dog said, "Cormac, look under your foot and lift an iron nail that you'll find there!"

Cormac looked under his foot, and lifted an iron nail that he found there. And the moment he took it up, it became a shining sword in his hand.

Said the little brown dog, "Cormac, that's the Sword of Victory. It is yours, because you were good to the pups. With that Sword you can vanquish the greatest champions in the world—with only one exception, and that is the Giant called Crohore of the Four Heads. The Sword cannot kill him, because his soul is not in his body. As you are not likely to meet him in all your travels," said the little dog, "you will always be able to win with that Sword, wherever you go. But if you ever find yourself in any terrible difficulty, and unable to extricate yourself, call three times upon me, the Cu-beag of the Willow-Wood, and I'll instantly appear, and do what I can to help you."

Cormac thanked the Cu-beag right heartily, and the little brown dog trotted back with the cake to her pups. Cormac did not lie down to sleep, but went forward again, with the Sword of Victory buckled on him. He traveled away and away, where you wouldn't know day from night, or night from day, far further than I could tell you, and twice further than you could tell me, over high hills, low hills, sheep-walks, and bullock-tracks, the Cove o' Cork, and old Tom Fox and his bugle horn—till at length, one evening late, he saw a castle of seven towers in the distance.

Cormac said, "That castle may mean adventure, and maybe fortune." So he went up and knocked at the gates; and the King himself came to the gates, and looking down at little Cormac, asked him what did he want.

"I'm looking for service, sir," said Cormac.

"And what can you do?" said the King.

"I'm apt at most anything," said Cormac, "but I'm particularly handy at handling a sword."

The King he laughed, and said, "I'm afraid I cannot give you anything to do, for the only man I'm looking for now is one who can fight Giants."

"That," said Cormac, "is what I'm especially good at. And I'd rather be fighting Giants than eating bread and butter with sugar on top of it."

The King laughed again, and shook his head, and said, "I'm afraid you would not be much good against these Giants, for they're the most terrible in the world."

"It will cost you nothing to give me a trial," said Cormac.

"Well," said the King, "if you're bent on throwing away your life, I'm not the man to stand in your way." He said, "I'll engage you for a year and a day, and I'll give you your weight in gold for wages, and my beautiful daughter in marriage, if you're alive at the end of that time. The only duty you have to do is to carry every morning a can of water for my daughter's bathing from the Well of Beauty in the valley below."

"Humph," said Cormac, "not much of a duty, that."

"Oh, but," said the King, "there are three terrible Giants who claim the ownership of that Well, and have killed every champion that ever undertook to carry a can of water from it. A thousand of the world's greatest champions have gone to that Well for water, but none of them ever returned alive."

"Well," said Cormac, "I'll do my best, and the best can do no more."

Very well and good. Cormac had a fine supper and a soft bed. And he was awakened in the middle of the night by the terrible roaring of three Giants in the valley. After breakfast the next morning, Cormac, getting a can from the King, started to the valley to fetch a can of water from the Well of Beauty.

Half-way down he saw a sight which surprised him—a terrible, big Giant with four heads, bound with willows, and tied up to the branch of a tree. The Giant said, "Good-luck to you, Cormac." But Cormac took no notice of him.

He reached the Well safely, and was dipping in his can, when he heard such a terrible roar as made the teeth in his head rattle. Jumping up, there he saw standing over him a great Giant with one head.

"You are too big for one bite and too small for two," said the Giant of the one head, "so I'll let you choose how to lose your life—whether with a swing by the back, a cut of the sword, or a square round of wrestling."

"Why, if it's the same to you," said the manly little Cormac, "I'll choose a cut of the sword."

So the Giant drew his sword, and Cormac drew his Sword of Victory, and to fighting both of them fell. They fought up and they fought down, and they fought round, and they fought over seventeen acres of ground. And such a fight was never seen in the world before or since. But at length, when the Giant was nearly exhausted, Cormac gave a skip, a leap, and a bound, and landed with his Sword right upon the Giant's neck, and cut the head off his shoulders. Then he filled his can with water at the Well of Beauty, and set out for the castle.

On his way he had to pass again the Giant of the Four Heads, who was tied up to a great branch of a tree. And the Giant said, "I gave you good-luck going down, Cormac, and as you're coming back the winner, I know you will be so kind as to cut me down, and free me."

"Let whoever tied you up, cut you down," said Cormac. "It wasn't your good deeds left you there, anyhow." And he went off.

The King was the first man Cormac met at the castle, and mightily surprised was he to see Cormac return.

The King said, "Cormac, had you any trouble getting the can of water this morning?"

"Oh, no trouble worth mentioning, sir," said Cormac.

"Well," said the King, "that surely astonishes me. But I'm afraid you'll not find it so next morning."

"Let every day look out for itself," said Cormac. "I never believe in worrying about next year's winds." And as he had his task done for that day, he went and enjoyed himself.

Next morning, when the King came to give the can to Cormac, he said, "It is a strange thing, Cormac, but I heard the roaring of only two Giants last night—whatever can be the meaning of it?"

"Maybe," said Cormac, "one of them was too sleepy."

"It must have been that," said the King.

Off Cormac started with his can for the Well of Beauty, in the hollow. And half-way down, he passed the tree from which the Giant of the Four Heads was hung. And the Giant, as he passed, said, "Good-luck, Cormac." But Cormac took no notice.

Cormac reached the Well of Beauty, and was just dipping in his can, when he heard an awful roar that made the teeth in his head rattle. Jumping up, there he saw a terrible Giant with two heads, standing over him.

"You're too big," said the Giant of the Two Heads, "for one bite, and too small for two, but I'll leave you your choice of how to lose your life —whether a swing by the back, a cut of the sword, or a square round of wrestling."

"Why," said Cormac, "if I must lose my life, I think I'd sooner lose it by a cut of the sword than any other way."

"Very well," said the Giant of the Two Heads.

And he drew his sword, and Cormac drew his Sword of Victory, and to fighting both of them fell. They fought up and they fought down, and they fought round, and they fought over thirty-four acres of ground. And the like of such a fight was never seen in the world before or since. At long and at last when the Giant was nearly exhausted, Cormac took a skip, a leap, and a bound, and landed with his Sword upon the Giant's neck, and cut off his two heads from his shoulders.

Then he filled his can from the Well of Beauty, and started for the castle.

As he passed the tree from which the Giant of the Four Heads was hanging, the Giant spoke out and said, "I gave you good-luck going down, Cormac, and as you are coming back the winner, I know you'll be so kind as to cut me down, and free me."

Said Cormac, "Let whoever tied you up, cut you down. It's not your good deeds that left you there, anyhow." And he went on.

The King was the first man who met Cormac at the castle, and right surprised he looked.

"Cormac," said the King, "I'm astonished to see you coming back alive. Had you no trouble in getting the can of water?"

"Oh, no trouble worth mentioning, sir," said Cormac.

"Well," said the King, "you have come back alive two mornings, but Cormac, you'll never come home the third."

"Let every day look after itself," said Cormac. "I never worry about next year's winds." And as his task was done for the day, he went and played and enjoyed himself.

Next morning when the King gave the can to Cormac, he said, "It's a very strange thing, but I heard only one Giant roaring last night—whatever is the matter?"

Said Cormac, "The other two must have been sleepy."

"That must have been it," said the King.

And Cormac started off with his can for the Well of Beauty.

Half-way down, he passed the Giant of the Four Heads tied up to the branch of a tree, and the Giant said, "Good-luck, Cormac." But Cormac took no notice of the fellow.

Down to the Well he went, and he was just dipping in his can, when he heard a terrible roar that made the teeth in his head rattle. Up jumped

Cormac, and there was an awful Giant with three heads, standing over him.

"You are too big for one bite, and too small for two," said the Giant of the Three Heads. "I'll leave you your choice of how to lose your life— whether by a swing by the back, a cut of the sword, or a square round of wrestling."

"Well," said Cormac, "if I must lose my life, I think I'd sooner lose it by a cut of the sword than any other way."

"All right," said the Giant, drawing his sword. And Cormac drew his Sword of Victory, and to fighting both of them fell. They fought up, and they fought down, and they fought round, and they fought over fifty-one acres of ground. Such a fight was never seen in the world before or since. At length when the Giant was nearly exhausted, Cormac took a skip, a leap, and a bound, and landed with his Sword upon the Giant's neck, and cut the three heads from his shoulders. Then he filled his can and started for home.

But when Cormac was half-way up the hill, and passing the tree from which the Giant of the Four Heads hung, the Giant said, "I gave you good-luck when you were going down, Cormac, and now that you're returning the winner, I know you'll be so kind as to cut me down, and set me free."

Now Cormac was such a good-hearted fellow, that he couldn't bear to see even the worst in the world suffering distress. So he said, "Oh! you have me pestered, every time I pass here, and I'll cut you down rather than be listening to you any longer."

So he took out his Sword, and cut the willows that bound the Giant of the Four Heads to the tree, and the Giant dropped off.

And the minute the Giant of the Four Heads found his feet, he drew his sword and said to Cormac, "You rascal, you have taken the lives of my three brothers, and now I'm going to take yours!"

"You vagabond!" said Cormac, drawing his Sword of Victory, "I'll soon leave your heads as low as your brothers'! maybe you don't know that I have the Sword of Victory which can vanquish all people in the world."

The Giant of the Four Heads laughed heartily, and said, "Cormac, there's one man in the world that your Sword of Victory has no power against,

190

and that is the Crohore of the Four Heads, whose soul is not in his body—and I'm that man."

When Cormac heard that he was the Crohore of the Four Heads, he knew he was beaten. But he bravely said, "I defy you anyhow!"

Said the Giant, "As you were so good as to cut me down, I'll not take your life, but only tie you up in my stead."

So he bound Cormac with willows, and tied him up to the branch. Then Crohore made a raid on the castle, and carried off the King's beautiful daughter.

The King and all his court set out in search, and the first thing they found was Cormac tied up to the tree.

"How did you come here?" said the King.

And Cormac told him how he had cut down the Crohore, and the Crohore had tied him up in his stead.

"Oh, you rascal!" said the King. "It took ten years and ten thousand men to catch Crohore and tie him up to that tree, and you loosed him again, and ended all my work, and lost me my daughter! Before we go further, after the Crohore, we'll first hang you for what you've done."

Poor Cormac was downhearted and grieved when he heard this, and begged that the King would give him one chance for his life.

"What chance do you want?" said the King.

"This chance," said Cormac. "I'll undertake to set out this minute, and I promise never to sleep two nights in the same house, nor eat two meals' meat at the same table, till I have found the castle of the Crohore, and rescued your daughter."

Said the King, "For a year and a day then, Cormac, your life will be spared, to see if you can succeed."

And Cormac, setting off, traveled away and away, where you wouldn't know day from night, or night from day, far further than I could tell you, and twice further than you could tell me, over high hills, low hills, sheep-walks and bullock-tracks, the Cove o' Cork, and old Tom Fox and his bugle horn—till, at length, one night late Cormac reached a little house in a dark wood, with one little old man in it, and the little old man welcomed him by name as Cormac, the King of Donegal's son, and asked him where he was going.

"I'm going searching for the castle of Crohore

of the Four Heads," said Cormac. "Maybe you could help me to find it."

Said the old man: "A third of the castles of the world I know, but the castle of the Crohore I don't know, nor do I want to know it. You will never find the terrible Crohore, and if you did, it would be better for you had you never found it. Take my advice, and go back home."

"I'll not go back home," said Cormac. "I have promised never to sleep two nights in the same house, nor eat two meals' meat at the same table, till I have found the castle of the Crohore, and rescued the King's daughter. And I'll keep my promise or perish."

"Very well," said the old man. "If you are bent on going, go you must, and I'll do what I can to help you."

In the morning, after breakfast, the old man took out Cormac, and mounted him on a horse, which had wings to its feet.

"With the speed of the wind this horse can go, Cormac," said the old man. "Get on his back, and you will reach tonight my elder brother's house, who'll be able to help you further, because he has lived two hundred years longer in the world than I, and knows four times as much about it. And," said the old man, "if you are ever in great distress call three times on me, the Gray Hawk of the Beechwood."

Cormac thanked him, mounted the horse and started—sweeping through the skies, his horse's heels touched only the hilltops—and on they sped, till, late, that night, he reached a little house on the edge of a lake in a dark wood, and he saw there a very old man, who welcomed him by name as Cormac, the King of Donegal's son. And he said, "I see, Cormac, that you stopped at my younger brother's house last night. Tell me where you are going, and what's your errand."

Cormac told him, and asked if the old man could help him.

The old man said, "I have lived four hundred years in the world, and know half of the castles in the world, but I don't know the castle of the Crohore. You had better go back home, for you'll never be able to find him. And if you did find him, it would be better for you had you never found him."

"I'll not go back home," said Cormac. "I have promised never to sleep two nights in the same house, nor eat two meals' meat at the same table, till I have found the castle of Crohore and rescued the King's daughter. And I'll keep my promise or perish."

"Very well," said the old man. "Then, I'll do what I can to help you."

After breakfast the next morning the old man took Cormac out, and plucked a lily from his garden, and blew on it. Immediately it was a beautiful balloon floating in the air, and waiting for Cormac to get in.

"That balloon," said the old man, "will take you through the skies with the speed of the lightning. You'll reach our eldest brother's house this night. He has lived two hundred years longer in the world than I, and knows ten times as much about it. Maybe he will be able to help you. And if ever you are in any great distress, and need my assistance, call three times on me, the Black Otter of Lough Finn."

Cormac thanked him right heartily, and set off through the skies with the speed of the lightning. He sped away and away, till, late that evening, he landed at a little house on the edge of the ocean, and going in, found there, one very, very old man, who welcomed him by name as Cormac, the King of Donegal's son. And he said, "I see that you stopped at my two younger brothers' houses, these two last nights. Sit down and tell me where you are going, and what's your errand."

And Cormac told him, and asked if he could direct him to the castle of Crohore.

Said the old man, "I have lived in the world for six hundred years, and in all that time, I only once reached the castle of Crohore, so far is it out of the world. I advise you to go back, for you can never reach it. And, besides, if you ever did find it, it would be far better that you had never found it."

"I'll not go back," said Cormac, "for I have promised never to sleep two nights in the same house, nor eat two meals' meat at the same table, till I have found the castle of Crohore, and rescued the King's daughter. I mean to keep my promise or perish."

"Very well," said the old man. "Then, I'll do all I can to help you."

And in the morning after breakfast, he took Cormac down to the ocean's edge, and plucking a May-flower, laid it on the water, where immediately it was a full-rigged ship.

Said the old man: "This ship goes with the speed of the sunlight. Get into it, and it will take you to the land where the Crohore lives. After that, you will have to find your own way. But if you are ever in great distress, and need my help, call three times upon the Blue Hern of the Billows."

Right heartily Cormac thanked him, and off he went in his magic ship, sailing with the speed of the sunlight, till, that evening late, it ran up upon the shore of a far land—and Cormac got out and slept on the shore. And in the morning he went forward, and traveled away and away, where you wouldn't know day from night, or night from day, far further than I could tell you, and twice further than you could tell me, over high hills, low hills, sheep-walks, and bullock-tracks, the Cove o' Cork, and old Tom Fox and his bugle horn. Till at long and at last one evening late he sighted a great castle of ten tall towers in a dark wood.

As he came near the castle he saw, looking from a window in the tallest tower, no other than the King's daughter herself, whom he had come to rescue, the most beautiful damsel in all the world. She waved with delight to Cormac when she saw him, and Cormac came to the bottom of the tower. She told him that this was the castle of Crohore, and that he held her a prisoner there. Crohore, she said, wanted her to marry him—but she had asked for a year and a day's freedom before she would give her consent—in hope that she might be rescued. He had granted her request. The greater part of the year and a day was now up, and she had begun to despair of ever escaping.

"And I'm afraid, Cormac," she said, "by venturing yourself here you have only thrown away your life."

"Well," said Cormac, "it will be thrown away in a good cause."

"Cormac," she said, "Crohore, who is away hunting, will soon be returning; and you had better go to a little house that is in the valley, and hide yourself till the Crohore has gone to the hunt again to-morrow."

Said Cormac, "As you know, the Crohore cannot be killed because his soul is not in his body. I want you to try and find out, tonight, where his soul is. Then we'd have chance of escaping."

She promised to do her best to find this; and Cormac went off and hid in the valley.

When the Crohore returned from the hunt that night, the Princess came to him after his supper, and for the first time since he had carried her away, discoursed pleasantly with him. As soon as she thought she had him in a good humor, she said, "If you want me to love you, why do you keep your secrets from me?"

"What secrets am I keeping from you?" asked the Crohore.

"You have never told me where your soul is," said she.

"Oh," said Crohore, "my soul is in the great rock on the lawn in front of the hall-door."

Very well and good. Next day she told the news to Cormac.

"I'm sure it isn't there," said Cormac. "But, nevertheless, we'll test it." So, by Cormac's directions, the Princess decorated the rock—hung flowers around it, and put gold and silver ornaments upon it till it looked rich and grand.

When Crohore returned from the hunt that evening, and saw how she had decorated the rock where his soul was supposed to be, he was right well pleased. And he said to her that night, after supper, "It's a pity to waste all your beautiful work, and all your pretty flowers and valuable ornaments, on that old rock—for, after all, my soul isn't there. I only told you that to test you; and now that I see you really love me, I'll tell you where my soul is. It is in the beech-tree at the east of the house."

When she told this to Cormac next day, Cormac said, "I don't think it is in the beech-tree either. However, just to try him," Cormac said, "decorate the beech-tree today."

So she hung the beech-tree with lovely flowers, and beautiful ribbons, and gold and silver ornaments. And when Crohore returned he was mightily pleased at the sight. Now he was fully convinced that the King's daughter at length loved him. So, after supper, he said to her, "I see now that you certainly do love me, and I'll tell you where my soul really is, for it is not in the beech-tree."

"Where is it?" she asked.

He said, "In the center of the garden grows a green holly-tree."

"I know it," she said.

Said Crohore, "My soul is in that holly-tree,

but still no one can hurt or harm it, because even if the holly-tree were cut down, my soul would escape in a fox, that would jump out of the heart of the holly-tree, and there's no dog in all the world can catch that fox—except one dog, the Cu-beag of the Willow-Wood. Even if the fox were killed, out of the fox would fly a wild duck with my soul in it. And there's nothing in all the world could catch that wild duck—except the Gray Hawk of the Beech-Wood. And if that wild duck were caught and killed, out of the wild duck would drop an egg with my soul in it. The egg would fall to the bottom of the deepest lake in the world, and nothing in all the world could bring up that egg—except the Black Otter of Lough Finn. Even if that egg were brought up and opened, my soul would escape out of it in an eel, which would swim into the River Shannon, and curl under a stone in the deepest pool there, and nothing in all the world could find that eel—except the Blue Hern of the Billows. Even then my soul would hide in the head of the eel, and I could never be killed till the eel's head was cut off, and I was struck with it on the black spot that's on the back of my throat. Then and then only would I be killed.

And all that, as you see, is impossible for all the world to accomplish."

Next day, when Crohore was gone to the hunt, she told Cormac the news. And Cormac said, "Well, we have found his secret at last, and, with the help of Heaven, will destroy this villain."

He asked for the sharpest and heaviest hatchet in the castle, and with it he went into the garden, and began to cut down the green holly-tree. At the first stroke, Crohore, who was hunting in the woods thirty miles away, gave a roar that shook every window in the castle, and the sound of which went three times round the world. And Crohore that moment started for home.

Cormac laid on the holly-tree with the hatchet with all his might—for he found the earth trembling as Crohore came. And at every stroke Cormac gave, Crohore put out of him another roar that rattled the stars. And at every piece that Cormac cut from the holly-tree, the Crohore, running for home, was growing weaker. When he came within sight of his castle, Cormac, feeling that his life was now on the speed of his work, with one blow cut the tree through. Crohore that instant staggered, and only saved himself from falling.

But he gave a cry that startled the birds from all the woods of the world, and sent them to the skies in terror.

When the holly-tree fell, out of the heart of it jumped a fox, and away like the wind. Cormac called three times on the Cu-beag of the Willow-Wood, which instantly appeared, sped after the fox, and killed it.

And Crohore, who was now getting near Cormac, was weaker and foaming with rage.

When the fox was killed, out of it flew the wild duck, who mounted the skies like a rocket. Three times Cormac called upon the Gray Hawk of the Beech-wood, which immediately swooped in sight, and after the wild duck, killing it in the clouds.

Cormac now saw the Crohore closer and closer upon him, and, weak as he was, he was still terrible enough to kill a hundred men.

When the wild duck was killed, from it fell an egg, which went to the very bottom of a deep lake. Cormac called three times upon the Black Otter of Lough Finn, who answered his call right quickly, and dived to the bottom of the lake and brought up the egg.

Still nearer now was the raging Crohore, and

in very few minutes he would be on Cormac and have his life.

When the Black Otter brought up the egg, it broke, and out of it sprang an eel, which swam into the River Shannon, curling itself under a stone in the deepest pool there. Loudly, my brave Cormac called three times upon the Blue Hern of the Billows. And immediately the Blue Hern appeared, dived for the eel, brought it up, and dropped it at the feet of Cormac, who took the head off it immediately.

The Crohore, now staggering with weakness, but still terrible enough to have the lives of ten men, was within three bounds of poor Cormac, and his mouth as open wide as a castle-window with rage.

Through the wide-open mouth Cormac saw the black spot at the back of his throat. Taking good aim, he threw the eel's head, and struck the spot squarely. That instant, Crohore gave a roar that rattled the stars, and deafened all ears in the world for an hour—and he fell dead at Cormac's feet.

The King's daughter, who had been watching from her tower, gave three cries of joy, and came down and joined Cormac. From the Giant's castle, and the Giant's vaults, they filled their magic ship with jewels and pearls, precious ornaments, and bags of gold and silver—and then set sail. And they never stopped till they reached her father's castle, which they did on the very day that the year and the day was expiring.

Great was the rejoicing by the King and all the court, who had now given both of them up for lost. A wedding was ordered, and the King asked in all the lords and ladies and all the nobles and all the knights of the land. And the magic ship went specially to Ireland for Cormac's father and mother, the King and Queen of Donegal, and brought them to the wedding likewise.

And in addition to all these, there were four very honored guests at the wedding—four to whom was given more honor than to all the other guests together—the Blue Hern of the Billows, the Black Otter of Lough Finn, the Gray Hawk of the Beech-Wood, and above all, Cu-beag of the Willow-Wood!

The wedding lasted nine days and nine nights, and the last day and night were better than the first.

The King gave his kingdom to Cormac and the

bride. They needed, to guard them, neither army nor navy, for the Hern, the Hawk, and the Otter, under noble command of the Cu-beag, watched their realm by sea and land.

And in peace and happiness all of them lived ever after.

THE THREE PRINCESSES
OF CONNAUGHT

ONCE upon a time when there were plenty of kings and queens—it's many of them we've heard of, but few of them ever we've seen except in drawings in parlors, and pictures in gentlemen's halls— there were three beautiful sisters, Princesses of Connaught, who were taken away by three giants. The King and Queen of Connaught, in great distress, they gave it out that whatever three champions would rescue them and bring them back would have them in marriage, and the Kingdom of Connaught divided among them.

Now, as you may guess, there was many's and many's the lad of high and low station, and both fair and ugly, who set out before them in hopes of finding the Princesses and rescuing them; and you may well suppose, too, it was few and very few of these lads ever came back to their homes at all.

Now there was one poor man in the hills o' Donegal, who hadn't much to live on, and who was in poverty more months of the year than he was in plenty, and he had one son, Conal, a brave, big, strapping, bold lump of a fellow, and maybe handsome too, if I say it.

Now doesn't this Conal get up one morning and begin speaking to his father.

"Father," says he, "I think I'll go and have a try for capturing the Princesses. Who knows but I'll be the luckiest lad of them all!"

'Tis sorry the father would be to lose his son Conal, for a great help entirely he always was to him. And he took some time to think over the matter, for he did not wish to advise him in any way that he might afterward regret. Then he said:

"Conal darling, don't leave me, for if you go on that wild-goose chase, it's never more I'll see the face of you."

"Father dear," says Conal, says he, "what is there at home but poverty, and cold potatoes; you have a big struggle to live upon the bit of land as it is, and one mouth will be easier filled than two. God's good," says Conal, says he, "and there's no saying what luck is afore me. I am come to the time of day now," says he, "that I should be going out into the world to push my fortune. And, 'Never venture, never win'—if I run a big risk sure the price is big too. And Father," says he, "if I succeed I'll not be forgetting you anyhow, but will soon lift you out of your poverty, and you can live in luxury all the rest of your days."

Well, there was nothing for it but for his father to give Conal a blessing, and three gold guineas in money, and shake his hand and wish him "God speed" and "soon and safe back again"—and then Conal was off, and the old man was left alone.

Now the first crossroads Conal came to he found a poor man sitting crying there, and Conal, who was always a kind-hearted poor boy, drew on him and asked him what was the matter, and the man told him he was that poor and that disabled that he could neither work nor want, and there was nothing but starvation lookin' him in the face.

Poor Conal put his hand in his pocket and handed him one of his three gold guineas, and then he went on; and the next crossroads he come to, he met another poor old disabled man who was crying with the same complaint, and poor

Conal put his hand in his pocket and gave him one of the precious gold guineas.

And when he come to a third crossroads he found a third poor man crying likewise over hardships and want, and the last gold guinea was in his pocket Conal took out and handed him; so that he left him without a penny to bless himself with. But he said he had his father's blessing, and the blessing of three poor men; and that was better than all the gold in Guinealand.

Well, on and on he traveled till he come to the ocean, and when he come there, what did he see but a captain taking two Princes aboard of a boat, and all of them making ready to sail away.

Conal, he asked them whither they were going, or what they were going to do; and the two Princes said this captain was fetching them to the Island of Grey Rocks and Long-billed Fowls, where they were going in quest of the three beautiful sisters, the Princesses of Connaught.

Conal asked to join them, but they said that was death for him, and they only laughed at him. Then he proposed to go as the captain's servant, and the captain packed him into the boat.

They sailed to the island, and when they come

there all four of them traveled to the top of a high hill, and there was a big round opening in the ground there that went down, down, down, till Conal could see no bottom to it.

Now they had carried with them a basket tied to the end of a long, long rope, and one of the Princes was put into this basket and lowered down through the hole, down and down till they had to let out a mile of the rope, and then the basket stopped and they knew that it had reached the island under the earth.

The young Prince had agreed with them that they were to watch the rope, and at the end of a year and a day if he was alive and well and had rescued the Princesses he would arrive back at the bottom again and shake the rope, and they would draw him and them up.

Very well and good. Away they went every man about his own business through the island, where they lived for a year and a day, and at the end of a year and a day the three of them met at the hole. They observed the rope, but not a shake nor shake did the rope get for all the day long, and then they knew that something had happened.

"Well," says the second Prince, "it's my turn now."

And down they let him, and parted with him on the same conditions that if at the end of a year and a day he was alive and well, he was to come and shake the rope.

But to make a long story short, when the year and a day was up and the captain and Conal went to the hole and watched the rope, there wasn't a shake nor a tremble in it for all the day long; and they then knew again that something had happened to him. And then says my bold Conal to the captain:

"I would like to try my chance at rescuing the three beautiful Princesses of Connaught, if you don't mind."

Very well and good, the captain had no objections, and on the same terms down he lets Conal; and down, and down, and down he went, till he thought he would never be done going down.

But at length and at last doesn't he reach the bottom where he finds a beautiful country with hills and dales and green woods stretching away and away from him as far as his eye could carry. And forward through this country my brave Conal starts, and on he traveled away and away far further than I could tell you, and twice as far as you could tell me, till at length and at last late one fine evenin' he came to a wee thatched house, with a red-headed man on top of it fixing the chimney, and Conal asked him if he could get a bite to eat, and a bed to lie on for the night.

"You can that," says the red-headed man, says he, coming down off the house, "but whether will ye stand me a good round of boxin' for a bite and a bed in the parlor, or have a bite and a bed in the kitchen free?"

"By all means," says Conal, says he, "a good round of boxin' for a bite and a bed in the parlor will be my choice."

And there and then both of them peeled off, and squared up and went at it like two men at a day's work, and they fought up and down, and rings around them, for as good as an hour; and the Red Fellow wasn't gettin' the better of Conal, nor Conal wasn't gettin' the better of the Red Fellow, though a harder, or a better, or a sharper fight Conal never had at home in Ireland; and it's many's the fight he had fought with bigger and stronger fellows in his day.

And at an hour's end when Conal was pretty well out of puff, and every bone in his body beaten sore, the Wee Red Fellow dropped his hands and he said, "That will do, Conal, I have got enough of it; ye're the best box man, barrin' one, that I fought with for this last three hundred years, and," says he, "that one was three hundred years older than myself, and so had the advantage of me. Come in," says he, "and make yourself at home in the parlor."

And when Conal went in what did he see but the two Princes, his comrades, lying stretched as if they were asleep, one by every side of the kitchen fire.

And says he to the Wee Red Man, "What's the meanin' of this?"

Says the Wee Red Man, "One of them chaps is lyin' in his sleep for twelve months, and the other for two years. When they come here asking for lodgings," says he, "and I gave them their choice like· I gave you last night, they both chose a bite an' a bed in the kitchen free. Droll lads they were," says he, "comin' to rescue Princesses; they were afraid to stand up to a wee old man for one round of boxin'."

So Conal saw they were enchanted; and indeed, he said to himself, it was enchanted they deserved to be, since they were cowards.

A good supper and a soft bed Conal had, and a hearty breakfast when he got up in the morning; and outside the Wee Red Man then fetched him, and gave him a hazel rod and a ram's horn, and a bushel of brass filings, and he directed him to get astride of the hazel rod, and that he would reach the castle of the one-eyed Giant, who had the three Princesses as his prisoners. And then he was to make up a plan with the three Princesses that they would escape with him in the middle of the night when everybody at the castle was fast asleep.

"The one-eyed Giant," says he, "has three stables, one of black horses, one of white horses, and one of chestnut mares; in the third stable of chestnut mares, there's three that stand farthest from the door; give the oldest Princess this bag of brass filings, and before they go to bed at night tell her to give each of those three mares a feed of these filings.

"In the middle of the night when the old fellow is asleep you are all to get out as quietly as you can; the three ladies will mount the three chestnut mares and you will mount the hazel rod, and when you are all right, sound your ram's horn three times and then don't wait on the wind to catch you, but ride for here."

Well and good, as he was directed Conal done. That evening he reached the Giant's castle. The Giant was from home, and it's the joy was in the hearts of the Princesses when they found a young stranger from Ireland to rescue them; but as the Giant was then coming home they hid him away in a tower at one end of the castle where he could not be discovered.

Everything was done as the Wee Red Fellow had ordered. The oldest Princess, before she went to bed, made three mashes of the brass filings and gave one to every one' of three chestnut mares; and when the old fellow was well asleep out the four of them went and mounted, and when they were mounted and ready Conal raised the ram's horn and gave three terrific blows on it.

At the first blow every door in the castle fell off it, and everything that wasn't solid masonwork fell down. At the second blow the castle itself shook and bent over, and at the third blow

the stars rattled in the sky and the castle come
to the ground, and out from the ruins leaps the
one-eyed Giant, the face of him black with rage
and fury, and he bounds for them; and that instant
off they started without waiting for the wind to
catch them, and so fast went the chestnut mares
that it was only the tops of the hills their feet
touched. But fast as they went the Giant himself was coming every bit as fast, and, if anything,
gaining on them.

But, behold ye! as they reached the hut of the
Wee Red Man he was outside waiting, and a wee
ball of yarn in his hand; and between them and
the Giant he steps, and he throws the ball of yarn
at him, and the yarn goes round him in a
circle of fire, and there and then he was standing
a big tall lump of a stone, and never a move could
he make.

In the morning the Wee Red Man touched
the two sleeping Princes with a white hazel rod,
and they jumped up to their feet as well as ever.

Says the Wee Red Man: "There's now three
pairs of ye, and when ye go back the King will
marry ye and divide up his kingdom amongst ye,
and a wedding-present I would like to give each

bride. Here," says he, "is three crowns for each, a crown of gold, a crown of silver, and a crown of copper. Now all three brides must be married together, and every one of them must wear her three crowns, there and then, that's the obligation I leave on each and every one of ye."

Right heartily they thanked the Wee Red Man.

He told them to stay in his house and rest themselves as long as they liked, and to go when they pleased, and then he himself went away and disappeared. And when they had waited to rest themselves as long as they liked, they set out, and they traveled away and away before them, and were traveling for long and for long, till at length and at last they reached the basket at the bottom of the hole.

They put each of the Princesses in, in turn, and shook the rope and she was hauled up, and then the Princes said they would go in turn, so that Conal was left to the very last.

And when they were all gone up except Conal, and it came his turn to go, something somehow struck him, and instead of getting into the basket himself he said he would try something else first, and he piled into it a lot of stones, and then shook the rope, and when the basket was hauled about half up, didn't it and the rope come tearing, tumbling down again; for as Conal had suspected, the cruel captain and two Princes above cut the rope and let it drop. Their intention was, of course, that poor Conal would be killed and done with forever out of their road.

And then the captain and two Princes set out with the three Princesses for their home, and brought them there and said it was they who had rescued them.

Now Conal had with him the three crowns belonging to the youngest Princess, which he had been carrying for her. He went wandering about, below, in despair, not knowing what to do, and at length he said to himself he would travel back to the hut of the Wee Red Fellow and see if he could help him out of his dilemma. Perhaps he could tell him what to do.

But when Conal came to the hut it was deserted, and there was no one there, or no one to be seen, only there was plenty to eat and drink; so he settled down to live in it, and for a year and a day he lived there all by his lee alone.

At the end of that time, when he got up out of

his bed one morning, what does he see on the table but a lovely wee round skull-cap with gold lace on it. He knew well he hadn't put it there himself, and that it wasn't in the house before; and he wondered and wondered, but he thought it very nice, and when he went out for a walk in the garden he brought the cap with him and was admiring it. Then he put it on his head and tried how it fitted him. And after a little Conal says to himself, says he:

"The purty fit it is, and the purty cap, only sure there's no one to admire it on me here. I wish," says he, "it's at home in Ireland and near the King's castle in Connaught I was."

And lo and behold ye! that very instant doesn't he find himself walking by the wall of the King's castle at Connaught, and he rubbed his eyes hard, for he could scarcely believe his own senses. But it was awake he was sure enough, and at home, and not dreaming. He looked down at himself, and surely he looked a wonderful picture, for his clothes were tattered and torn, and well worn; and he thought to himself that his own mother if she was alive wouldn't know him in that distressful condition.

He walked till he came to a blacksmith's forge not far from the castle, and then he went in there and he asked for work, and the blacksmith asked what he could do. And Conal said he could do 'most anything that any handy man could, and the blacksmith hired him and Conal went to work with him and was a big help to him entirely.

Into the blacksmith's shop the neighbors they would drop every day to gossip about all the goings on, and to talk about what was a-doing at the castle; and Conal, he wasn't many days there when he heard that there was a great wedding to come off, for the three Princesses of Connaught were to be married to a captain and two Princes who had rescued them from a terrible Giant that had taken them away, and all the world was going to see the wedding, and they asked Conal to come, too.

And on the day of the wedding, Conal he rolled up his apron round him, and he went over to the castle with the crowds to see the marriage.

There was a big platform built in the castle yard on which the three Princesses were to be married all at the one time. The gathering that came to see them was the greatest that ever Conal had seen in all his life, and when the time come, out came the King and Queen first, and then the priest, and then the captain and Princes with the three Princesses, and all of them dressed in the most gorgeous silks and satins, and silver and gold. And up on the platform they went to be married.

But the minute the priest begun, down fell the platform and smashed into smithereens, and it was a miracle that any of them escaped without some of their bones being broken.

The wedding was put off that day, and before the next wedding-day come round the King had got a great goldsmith to make three crowns for the youngest sister, a gold one, a silver one and a copper one, identically like the three crowns that her other sisters had, and no one could have told them from the others.

And on this second wedding-day again all the three sisters were wearing their three crowns, and all the world and his wife was gathered there to see them married, and Conal had come, too, with his leather apron rolled up and tied round him. But again at the last minute just as the priest went to tie the knot, down fell the platform

into smithereens; and the three pairs and the
priest, it was the miracle of the world that their
bones were not made into powder.

Then the King and all of them saw that the
three crowns the youngest Princess wore were
not the right thing, and the King gave out that
if there was any goldsmith in the land who would
guarantee to make the right crowns for the youngest he would give her to him for a wife, and the
third of the kingdom; but if the crowns were
wrong the goldsmith would lose his head.

One great goldsmith was asked to do it, and
another, and another, but not one of them would
venture, for they didn't want to lose their heads
yet awhile; and then the King and everybody
didn't know what to do, and it was the whole talk
in Conal's master's forge among the people every
day.

At last says Conal, says he, to his master when
they were still at the forge one night:

"Would you undertake to make these crowns?"

"What do you mean?" says the master.

"I mean," says Conal, says he, "that I can make
them for you, if you only go to the castle in

the morning and say that you are going to make
the crowns, and that you want three pounds of
gold, three pounds of silver, and three pounds of
copper." And he talked over the master till he
persuaded him to do as he was bid.

And on the morrow sure enough the master
went to the castle and said he would undertake
to make the crowns, and he got the three pounds
of gold, three pounds of silver, and three pounds
of copper, and fetching them home with him he
gave them to Conal that he might make the
crowns.

Now Conal got ready the three crowns which
he had with him from the underworld, and that
evening when all the rest of the work was finished
Conal got the forge empty of everybody except
himself, and the gold and the silver and the copper, and his own crowns which he had kept without anybody ever seeing them, and the doors and
the windows were barred and stuffed so that nobody could see in. And Conal set the fire going
hard, and the people of the countryside were all
gathered outside round the forge listening to the
fire going, and the bellows blowing, and Conal

ding-donging and hammering and sledging away all the night long, and he every now and then shoving out scraps of gold and copper out through the windows, and the fellows all scrambling and fighting for the castaway scraps.

And in the morning Conal opened the doors and the windows and the people all flocked in, and their mouths and their eyes were opened with wonder when they saw the three beautiful crowns of gold, silver and copper that Conal had set on the anvil. And Conal sent the smith with them to the castle, making him pretend that it was he, himself, made them.

And when the King and the Princesses and all of them saw the three beautiful crowns and saw that they were as like the crowns of the other sisters as no mortal man could make them, they were astonished and delighted, and the smith was hailed as a genius.

And the King said at once that the smith should have the youngest daughter at marriage. And they washed the smith and dressed him up in silk and satin and gold and silver, and the marriage, it was ordered to come off at once.

And the people all gathered into the courtyard and the two Princes with their Princesses and the smith with his (for the captain was now left out in the cold).

They went onto the platform to get married; and the instant they did, the smith felt the platform beginning to shake, and he called out to stop the marriage, for it wasn't him made the crowns, at all, at all, but a poor journeyman who was working with him and who was now at home in the forge banging away at his work.

When the King heard this he sent one of his servants to the forge with a coach to fetch Conal in it.

Now Conal took his wishing-cap in his pocket and he stepped into the coach, and when the servant looked at the black and ragged picture of him as he was closing the coach door he says, "The Lord pity the poor Princess that is to take the likes of that fellow." And the coach door was closed on Conal and the coach started.

He put his wishing-cap on his head and wished that the coach might be filled with rotten cabbages and he himself be back in his forge again.

So when the coach drove into the King's yard
and the servant before them all went and opened
the coach door to let Conal out, down on top of
him falls and breaks scores upon scores of rotten
cabbages, and he was a spectacle and the people
chased him for his life out of the courtyard.

"I see," says the King, "it wasn't right of me to
send a common servant for Conal."

So he then orders one of his nobles to go with
the coach and fetch him. And when the noble
went to the forge and got Conal into the coach
and was closing the door upon him he shook his
head and says, "The Lord pity the poor Princess
who has to marry the likes of that tattered fellow."

Conal said nothing, only, when the coach was
well started, put on his wishing-cap again and
wished himself back in his forge and the coach
filled with old dirty brogues; so that when the
coach drove into the King's yard and the great
nobleman went and opened the door, down on
top of him falls the coachful of old dirty brogues,
and the people hunted him and he run for his
life.

"I see," says the King, "that I have insulted

227

that boy twice, and he going to be married to a
King's daughter and be a King himself. It is a
King should go for him and no one else."

So out he set himself, and when he come to the
forge there was Conal in his tatters banging away
at old iron.

The King made his lowest curtsey to him and
asked him wouldn't he do him the honor of step-
ping into his coach and coming to the castle to
marry his fairest daughter?

And Conal said he surely would; and he stepped
into the coach and the King closed the door and
sat up behind like a footman. And Conal put
on his wishing-cap as he went, and he wished to
be dressed in a dress becoming to a man who was
going to marry a King's daughter; so that when
the King opened the coach door in the courtyard
out of it there stepped the nicest, and bravest and
handsomest young man any of them had ever
seen before. And he dressed in the beautifullest
dress of silk and satin that ever they laid their
eyes on, and plenty of gold and silver lace all
over it. And when the young Princess laid eyes
upon him it's quickly she knew Conal and it's

deeply in love with him she was; for he was as handsome as herself, and that's saying a great deal indeed.

She flew to him and threw her arms around his neck and kissed him, and up on the platform she led him for the marriage.

It's right well and right heartily the two Princes were ashamed of themselves then, and they went on their knees to Conal before all the people, and confessed what they had done, and asked his pardon.

And my brave Conal didn't think they were worth spending a spite upon; so he told them to get up and to marry the Princesses, and there and then all three pairs of them were married together, and such a marriage and such rejoicement was never known in all of Ireland before nor since.

Conal sent to Donegal for his poor father and fetched him to the wedding, and the King bade him sit up beside himself, and the wedding lasted for a year and a day. The first day was as good as the last and the last as good as the first; and every other day of their lives was as happy as the best of them days.

I was at the wedding myself and got a bite of a pie for telling a lie, brogues of glass and slippers of bread, and came hopping home on my head. Only I ate all the good things I would have some of them now to give you.

THE MISTRESS OF MAGIC

ONCE upon a time, and a good time it was, there was a man in the mountains of Donegal who had one son, named Manus, who was growing up a fine, brave, nice boy entirely and a help and comfort to his father. But on a night doesn't there arrive at this man's house a Prince from the East with eleven of his followers, and he asked to be put up for the night, and Manus's father put him up and welcome. After supper the Prince from the East began putting his followers and himself through a lot of wonderful magical tricks which astonished Manus's father very, very much indeed. And he said he wished his son Manus could work tricks like that.

Said the Prince of the East, "How would you like it, if I took your son Manus with me and taught him Magic, too?"

"I would like it very well indeed," said Manus's

father. "Only I am very fond of Manus, and I wouldn't like to spare him long."

"Would a year and a day be too long?" said the Prince of the East.

"It would not," said Manus's father. "And if you'll promise to teach Manus your magical tricks and have him here again in a year and a day from now, you'll be doing me a great favor, and I'll willingly let you have him."

"Very well and good," said the Prince from the East, agreeing to that. I will take Manus with me, and verse him so well and soundly in magical tricks that when I bring him back to you in a year and a day, I promise that he'll astonish you."

The father was as well pleased at this as Manus; and Manus was as well pleased as the father. Next morning Manus bade the father farewell, and set off and away with the Prince of the East and his eleven followers.

The father, though he felt lonesome enough without his Manus, wrought hard and tried to be happy. Still, he couldn't help counting the time. And every day was a week to him, and every week was seven, till the year and a day were around, and he looked for his brave Manus again.

Right enough, on the very day when the year and a day were up, late in the evening, the Prince of the East arrived and Manus with him, and eleven other followers. And I tell you that was a glad meeting between Manus and his father. Manus was grown a bigger, and a stouter, and a braver, and a finer fellow far, than when he went away; and his father was proud of him. But if he was proud of him when he first saw him, he was double as proud when, after supper, the Prince of the East began to put Manus through his magical tricks, astonishing and priding the father at the wonderful things Manus could do.

"Ay," said the Prince of the East, "he is very good, surely for his time; but if the boy had only time enough it's a wonderful magician he would make. Wait till you see what these eleven and myself can do." And then he began to put his other eleven followers and himself through their tricks.

If Manus's trick had been great and fine, the tricks that the Prince himself and his eleven followers now went through astounded Manus's father out and out, and far surpassed anything Manus could do.

"Well, well, I wish and I wish," said the father, "that Manus had the ability of you twelve."

"And that he could have," said the Prince of the East, "if you only leave him long enough in his apprenticeship."

"How much longer do you want him?" said the father.

"Let us say a year and a day," said the Prince from the East. Although the father was grieved at the notion of parting with poor Manus again, still the temptation was great. So he agreed with the Prince that he should have Manus for another year and a day, provided he would fetch him back there to the same spot again at the end of that time, more perfect in Magic.

On the very next morning the father had to part with poor Manus again and a sad parting you may be sure it was. But the father said, "Manus, dear, keep up your heart and the year and a day will pass like a week—till you are with me again."

And off the Prince of the East and Manus and his other eleven followers set. And the father turned to his work and tried to be happy whilst the time went round, but every day was a week to

him, and every week was seven. looking forward
to Manus's coming again.

But the longest tale must have a finish, and the
lonesomest year an ending; so at long and at last,
the year and a day passed, and on the very last evening of the time, the Prince of the East with
Manus and his other eleven followers, they arrived
at Manus's father's in Donegal. And great and
great as was the joy of Manus's father at the meeting, just every bit as great was the joy of Manus;
and a happy pair they were that night.

The father laid down a royal supper for all of
them; and, when they had eaten and drunk to their
heart's content, the Prince of the East put Manus
on the floor and began putting him through his
tricks, for the father's delight. And if Manus had
been clever the first time, he was double as clever
now. And the father, delighted, said the like of
Manus for cleverness he had never seen before, and
that he'd now be as proud as a Prince for Manus
all the days of his life.

Said the Prince of the East, "Manus is good, and
very good—for his time. But if I had only long
enough of him, I would make him the most wonderful magician in the world again. Just wait till

you see," said he, "what these other eleven followers of mine can do." And he began putting
the other eleven followers and himself through
magical tricks. And if Manus's tricks had opened
his father's eyes, the tricks he now saw opened
them far wider surely.

And said he, "My son, Manus is good and very
good, as you say—but I only wish he was as good
as that."

"Will you let me have him for another year and
a day?" said the Prince of the East, "till you see
what I will make of him?"

"And a thousand welcomes," agreed the father.

Next morning sad enough was the parting; and
Manus again set out with the Prince of the East
and the other eleven followers. And the father,
he turned and went to his work and tried to feel
happy. But every day was a week to him, and
every week seven, till at long and at last the year
and a day were round. But at the end of the time
neither Prince nor Manus appeared. For, unfortunately, when the last agreement was made,
Manus's father forgot to put into it that he would
have to bring Manus back at the time's end. But
if Manus's father and Manus himself had over-

looked this point, the Prince of the East hadn't been blind to it—for he was a right cunning knave.

As restless as a hen on a hot griddle was the poor father all the dreary day, waiting and watching. But no Prince came, and alas! no Manus, although all the day he watched and waited, and all the night, and all the next day, too. With his heart nigh breaking, he got up early on the morning of the third day, and he took with him a cake of hard bread well-buttered, and set out to find the castle of the Prince of the East and fetch his Manus home. On and on before him he traveled till the sun was high, and himself hungry and tired as well. Then at midday he sat down, under a rowan-tree, to eat his cake and rest himself. And a gray hawk came flying and alit on the rowan-tree.

"Hungry, hungry I am," said the hawk. "Little old man, won't you divide your dinner with me?"

"It's little enough is it for myself," said Manus's father, "but I can't bear to see any of God's creatures go wanting." So he divided his cake with the hawk.

"You'll not lose by this," said the hawk. "There's only one creature in all the world knows

where that Prince's castle is, and it's I who only
have that knowledge," said the hawk. "I once put
the Prince under an obligation to me—and once I
went to his castle, but never went there again, for
it's almost beyond the world and a seven year's
journey to travel there. "But," said the hawk, I'm
so sorry for you that if you like to follow me, I'll
lead you there. By reason of the obligation I put
the Prince under I can get you entrance to his
castle. But I cannot tell you how you'll fare when
you get there."

"Thank you," said Manus's father. "And I'll
follow you if it was ten times as far."

Accordingly off they set with the hawk leading,
and flying ahead of Manus's father. When he
would be on the hill the hawk would be in the hollow, and when he would be in the hollow the hawk
would be on the hill.

And so it fared, and so he followed, while the
days grew to weeks, and the weeks to months and
the months to years—and the years grew to seven.
And on the night before the last day of the seventh
year the hawk told him they were now within a
day's journey of the Prince's castle, and that when

he reached it, he was to demand entrance and possession of his son in the name of the Gray Hawk of Knowledge—"which," the hawk said, "is my name. He'll have to give you both admittance and the chance of picking out your son among his twelve followers," said the hawk. "Only, when he puts the twelve before you to pick from, he'll be at liberty to have them in any shape he likes. No man will be able to tell one from another of them, so much alike will they be. And yet you'll have only one choice and must abide by it. It's heartily sorry I'll be if you fail. But may God bless you," said the hawk, "and send that you don't fail."

Right heartily Manus's father thanked the hawk and said, "Well, if I fail it won't be your fault anyway. You have surely done your best, now. And," he said sorrowfully, "the best can do no more."

Well and good. Towards evening of the next day he came in sight of a gorgeous castle of many towers—seated on a mountain-top and surrounded by great trees. And on the top of the highest tower alighted the Gray Hawk of Knowledge.

Manus's father now knew he had reached his journey's end. So, climbing up to the great castle

239

he knocked on the gates. And it was the Prince of the East himself who appeared.

"What is it you're wanting?" said he.

"I demand admission and search for my son," he replied, "in the name of the Gray Hawk of Knowledge."

The Prince of the East looked black when he heard this. But there was nothing for it but to open the gates and let him in. And the Prince said, "In the morning you'll be given chance of finding your son."

Manus's father got his supper and was shown to bed in one of the towers. But, just as he was about to fall asleep, he was aroused by a tapping on the window-pane. He got up and saw perched outside, a pigeon which was doing the tapping. He opened the window to the pigeon—and when it flew in, it turned into a young woman, the most beautiful, he thought, he had ever seen.

She said, "I'm the daughter of the Prince of the East; and, I must confess that I have fallen in love with your son, young Manus from Ireland. And it grieves me that my father has held him here under spells. And I now have come to help you to find him. Though," she said, "I must warn you that,

even if you find him, you'll still find it the hardest
task in the world to get him entirely free of my
father. In the morning my father will take you
out into the courtyard, and when he blows a whistle, twelve black birds will sit upon a tree and begin to sing, and you'll be asked to take your choice
of the twelve. They are my father's twelve followers, and your son is one of them. The way,"
says she, "you'll know your son is by his singing the
saddest song. Heaven send," said she, "that you
choose wisely. But, even then, your trouble will
only have begun." Then she turned into a pigeon
again, and flew out among the trees that surrounded
the castle.

In the morning the Prince of the East took
Manus's father into the courtyard. And he blew a
whistle, and twelve blackbirds appeared and
perched upon a tree, and all twelve began to sing.

Said the Prince, "Out of those twelve choose
your son."

One of the blackbirds sitting on the topmost
branch sang a song which was sad and very sad,
and forlorn entirely.

"I choose," said he, "that blackbird perched on
the topmost branch of the tree."

The Prince of the East looked as black as thunder. But there wasn't anything for it, but to turn the blackbird into the shape of a man again. And it was Manus. And he and his father embraced and cried for very joy.

With little delay they set out for home—on the very next morning. As they went along, the son said, "Dear Father, the Prince of the East doesn't mean to part with me easily. He'll surely come after us and try to get me from you by some trick or other. You are a poor man, Father," said Manus, "and if you manage well, I, by virtue of my magical knowledge, can get for you a good penny from the villain."

"How is that?" said the father.

Said Manus, "I'll turn myself into a sheep with a tether to me. You'll lead me along; and at twelve o'clock today you'll be met by a sheep buyer and eleven boys. He'll ask you what you'll take for the sheep. You say that this is a particular sheep, and you cannot part with it under a hundred pounds. He'll quickly close the bargain and pay you the money. Let him have the sheep, but on the peril of your life don't let away the tether. Then all will be well."

To this the father agreed: and into a sheep Manus turned himself, his father was driving him long with the end of the tether in his hold. And just at noon what should he meet up with but a sheep buyer, and eleven boys, who asked if he would sell the sheep.

"Yes," said Manus's father. "But as this is a particular sheep, I'll not part with it under a hundred pounds."

"You'll get your price," said the sheep buyer. And down he paid him a hundred pounds in gold, and took the sheep with him, Manus's father keeping the tether.

Then the sheep buyer pushed on his way with his eleven boys and his sheep, and Manus's father followed his way. And Manus's father wasn't three hours traveling, when who but his son overtook him. And both of them were rejoiced.

Next morning said Manus to his father, "My master doesn't mean to part with me as easily as you think. But if you do right today we'll get some more money out of the villain."

"How do you mean?" asked the father.

Said Manus, "I'll turn myself into a goat with a tether to it. You'll drive me before you, and at twelve o'clock you'll be met up by a goat buyer, and eleven boys. He'll ask you to sell him the goat; when you must say that this is a particular goat, and you wouldn't think of parting with it for less than two hundred pounds. He'll give you that, but you must be sure on the peril of your life not to part with the tether."

"All right," said the father.

So, turn himself into a goat Manus did, and his father drove him before him, the end of the tether in his hand. And, at twelve o'clock, sure enough, what does he meet but a goat buyer and eleven boys.

And said the goat buyer, says he, "Will you sell the goat?"

"I'll do that," said Manus's father. "But as this is a particular goat, I wouldn't think of parting with it under two hundred pounds."

"I'll give you that," said the goat buyer. And he did. He paid down to Manus's father two hundred golden pounds, and took away the goat before him—Manus's father slipping the tether off, and keeping it.

On then went Manus's father, and he wasn't

three hours traveling when up to him came Manus again. And both of them were rejoiced.

"We're doing well, Father," said Manus, "in punishing the villain. That's three hundred pounds you've got, and tomorrow if you act well, you'll have three hundred more."

"How is that?" asked his father.

"Tomorrow," said Manus, "I'll turn myself into a horse with a bridle. At twelve o'clock in the day, you'll meet an army captain with eleven dragoons, all armed with cutlasses; and the army captain will say that he is in want of a horse, and will ask you to sell him yours. You must say that this is a particular horse and you won't part with him under three hundred pounds. He'll buy me, but you be sure on the peril of your life not to let me away without first slipping off, and keeping, the bridle."

His father promised to do this.

Next day, Manus turned himself into a horse. And at twelve o'clock, right enough, up meeting them comes an army captain and eleven dragoons, every one of them armed with a cutlass. And the captain halted Manus's father, and told him he was in need of a horse. "I like the looks of that one you're leading," said he. "Will you sell him?"

"I'll sell him," said Manus's father. "But as he's a very particular horse, I wouldn't think of parting with him under three hundred pounds."

"I'll give you that," said the army captain. "But come," said he, "to this inn till I pay you the money, and we've a drink over it."

To the inn with them, unfortunately, went Manus's father, who got his three hundred golden pounds paid there, and had a drink with them over it. That drink led to a second, and the second to a third, till in the end poor Manus's father forgot about the bridle. Off went the captain, and his eleven dragoons, taking with them the horse and the bridle also. And although Manus's father waited three days and three nights his son never came. And off, he set to seek his son again.

Now the Prince of the East rode Manus home, for of course it was he who was the army captain. With his followers there he held a council; and it was decided Manus should be punished by being roasted to death in a mill-kiln.

So, on the very next day they put Manus into

the mill-kiln, from which there was no escape, and they built the grate under.

Now the beautiful Princess who loved him, was in sore distress when she found they were burning her lover in the mill-kiln. Calling up all her magical power, she turned the millrace into the kiln, leaving it then to Manus's own powers to extricate himself.

The minute the water flowed in on top of him, Manus turned himself into an eel, and in the flow of water swam out into the river.

Then the Prince of the East and his eleven followers turned themselves into twelve otters, and dived into the river after him. Manus curled himself under the deepest stone in the river. But the otters searched every stone till they came to the right one.

When he found himself discovered, Manus turned himself into a white pigeon, and flew for the woods. But into twelve hawks turned the Prince and his followers, and away after Manus.

Swift and very swift was their flight, and close and very close the chase; till at long and at last the white pigeon tired and weakened and must

247

soon give up. And the hawks were fast closing on it. A castle was near at hand towards which the white pigeon, in extremity, flew. Just as it came to the castle, the ballroom window was thrown open, and a beautiful lady appeared at it and waved on the white pigeon to come that way. And this beautiful lady was none other than the Princess herself who had flown there before him. For this was the castle of her mother's brother.

In at the window flew the white pigeon, turned itself into a ring and went upon the Princess's finger.

In this great room was a party of ladies and gentlemen dancing and feasting. The twelve hawks, when they arrived, changed themselves into six fiddlers and six pipers, came under the ballroom window, and began to play the most enchanting airs ever heard, so that all the assembled lords and ladies flocked to the window to look and to listen. And when they had finished playing, the King of the castle was so grateful to them, that he bade them ask any reward they wished, and they should have it.

"We only ask," said the leader of them, "the ring upon that fair young lady's finger."

"You shall surely have that," said the King.

But the Princess took the ring from her finger, and threw it into the heart of the blazing fire.

That minute they turned themselves into six bellows, and six bellows blowers, and blew till they blew the ring out upon the floor. Into six blacksmiths and six sledges they then transformed themselves, and began to batter and beat at the ring. The ring went up in a burst of sparks and the sparks fell over the room in a shower of wheat. And into twelve geese they then changed, and began to eat the wheat—when the wheat turned into a fox, and took the heads off the twelve geese.

Then the fox changed itself into Manus in his own form again. And he and the Princess embraced and kissed each other. And when the King and the lords and ladies heard the whole story it is surprised and delighted they were.

It was agreed that they should be married within a week. All who were there were bidden to the wedding—and ten who weren't there for the one that was. Manus sent for his father to Donegal, and brought him there. Their wedding lasted nine days and nine nights—and the last day and night was better and merrier than the first.

After the wedding the three of them went to the castle of the Prince of the East, which Manus and his wife now heired and owned, and there they lived happy ever after.

THE PRINCESS SUIL-DUBH *

THERE was a young Prince in Donegal one time, long, long, and long ago, whose name was Rory Og O'Donnell. He was fond of the chase and especially fond of hunting the deer. One day, on the marshes, not far from his father's castle, he raised a red deer which led him fast and fetched him far, till he lost all his followers and even his dogs. But he stuck to the deer till at length it reached the banks of the River Erne—across which it swam and disappeared.

Rory came home disappointed. But on the marshes next day, at the same spot, he raised the same deer and in the same way followed it till it left him on the banks of the Erne. But though he lost the deer on the banks of the lovely river, he found himself in the nick of time to save the life of the most beautiful black-eyed maiden his eyes had ever beheld. She had lost control of a

* *Suil-dubh* is Irish (Gaelic) for *Black-Eye.*

curragh [canoe] which she was paddling, and was being swept to the falls, when Rory Og appeared on the banks. He plunged into the river and, at the risk of his own life, saved hers. But he would have risked a thousand lives to save another such beautiful damsel.

She was grateful and said, "As I have some magical powers, for your bravery and goodness I'll grant you any three reasonable wishes you ask."

Rory Og said, "A deer has just escaped me here for the second time. Since I am certain to raise him tomorrow, I wish for a bridge over the Erne at this spot; for a road through the marshes beyond; and you for my wife."

The damsel blushed, and said, "You will have the first two wishes. But for your own sake, I beg that you'll alter your third. I'm the Princess Suil-dubh, and the man who'll win me has to face fearful terrors and do things that are impossible to mortals."

"No matter for that," said Rory Og. "Your beauty and your modesty have so won my heart that it would be sweeter to die seeking you than to live in misery without you, even if all the world were mine."

The damsel, smiling, said, "Well, if you are prepared to brave all dangers, there's just a chance that you may win me. Good-by for the present, but follow your deer tomorrow. We'll meet before long."

The maiden disappeared beyond the river, and Rory Og rode home.

On the following day, Rory Og, out on the marshes, raised the same red deer at the same spot, and chased it to the River Erne, which it swam. But when Rory Og reached the river, he found there a beautiful bridge, over which he went like the wind. And through the marshes on the other side, which no man could travel before, was a hard road over which he rode fast and far on the track of the deer. But the deer always kept its distance ahead of him. When he was on the hilltop, the deer was in the next hollow, and when he reached the hollow, the deer was on the next hilltop.

At length night fell on him, without his overtaking the deer, and he found himself all alone in a wild country, over which he wandered long before he saw a light. Riding toward the light, he discovered a castle on a hillside, and an old man greeted him at the gates, saying, "You're welcome, Rory Og from Donegal." He bade him enter, and treated him to a fine supper and a soft bed.

As the old man left Rory Og in his bedroom, he said, "The snows are beginning to come down, and you must not be alarmed, no matter how fast they fall."

"Oh!" said Rory Og, "sleeping in such a strong castle as this, I don't care if all the snows in the heavens should fall."

He wasn't well in bed, however, when the falling snows came so fast and so thick and so heavy that the windows of his room were crushed in, and the snows came blowing into the room; every snowdrop the size of a saucer. He had himself well covered, but the snows piled mountain-high on top of him—as well as filling every nook, cranny, and corner of the room; and he felt the castle quivering with the pressure of the snows and quaking with their weight. The cold of the piles of them that were on top of him pierced him to the marrow of his bones, and he shivered so that he shook loose the nails of his toes.

The old man appeared in the morning, took him out, and asked him what kind of night he had.

"To tell you truth," said Rory Og, "I had the worst and terriblest night of my life, and if I should live to be a very old man, I wouldn't take the wealth of Africa and spend such a night again."

The old man said, "I am the Master of the Snows. This is only the first taste of the terrors you have to go through before you win the Princess Suil-dubh. I gave you this taste of the dangers because I am your friend, and wish you to turn back before it is too late."

When Rory Og heard that, he said, "I'll not turn back. If the dangers are a thousand times as dangerous, and the terrors a thousand times as terrible, I mean to win for my wife the Princess Suil-dubh, or perish."

"Very well," said the Master of the Snows. "I admire your courage, and right well you deserve her if you win her."

He gave Rory Og a good breakfast. After breakfast he said, "You can now mount your horse, and follow the deer forward. Whether you go fast or whether you go slow, you will tonight reach the castle of a half-brother of mine, who will entertain you for the night."

Rory Og thanked him, mounted his horse, and rode off; but he hadn't gone a hundred yards when the deer sprang out before him, and off. Rory followed fast after, but the deer kept its distance. When he was on the hilltop the deer was in the hollow, and when he reached the hollow, the deer was on the next hilltop. And so he fared till night fell on him, and the deer disappeared. Wandering on, he saw a light, and, riding toward it, found a castle.

An old man greeted him at the gates, saying, "You are welcome, Rory Og from Donegal. Come in and rest."

A good supper Rory Og got, and a soft bed. Before the old man left him in his bedroom, he said, "The rains have begun to come down, but don't be alarmed at anything that may happen."

Said Rory Og, "In a castle as strong as this, I don't care if all the rains in the heavens should rain tonight."

"That's good," said the old man.

But Rory wasn't well in bed when the lashing
and the slashing of the rains on the windows became frightful. Very soon the windows were
burst in, and the rain poured in, in floods. Every
drop would fill a bucket, and at every new gust
of rain the castle rocked to its foundations. Very
soon the room filled, till Rory Og had only his
nose above water. And in that terrible state he
was all night.

The old man came in the morning, and said,
"Rory Og, what kind of night did you pass?"

Rory Og replied, "The most terrible night of all
my life, and if I live to be a very old man, I
wouldn't pass another such frightful night for
the wealth of Africa."

Said the old man, "I am the Master of the
Rain. Last night was only to give you a taste of
the terrors and dangers that are ahead of you, if
you will persist in following the Princess Suil-
dubh."

Said Rory Og, "I don't care if the terrors are
a thousand times more terrible, and the dangers
a thousand times more dangerous, I'll never stop
or rest till I have found out, and won, the Princess
Suil-dubh."

"Well," said the Master of the Rain, "I admire
your courage, and you well deserve her if you
win her. Take your breakfast now, and then follow the deer. Whether you go fast or whether
you go slow, you'll reach this evening the castle of
another half-brother of ours, who will entertain
you for the night."

Rory Og thanked him, and after breakfast mounted his horse and rode off. But he
hadn't gone a hundred yards, when he raised the
deer, and followed it as before. But whether he
went fast or slow, the deer always kept its distance.
When Rory was on the hilltop the deer was in
the hollow, and when Rory reached the hollow the
deer was on the next hilltop. And so they fared
till evening fell on him, and the deer disappeared;
while Rory wandered about, not knowing where
he was. At length he saw a light, and, going toward it, came to a castle.

An old man greeted him at the gate, saying,
"You are welcome, Rory Og from Donegal. Come
in and rest."

A fine supper he gave Rory that night, and a
soft bed. And before he left him in his bedroom,
the old man said, "The wind has been rising, but

do not be surprised or alarmed at anything that may happen to you tonight."

"In such a strong castle as this," said Rory, "I don't care if all the winds in the heavens blow tonight."

"That's good," said the old man, and left him.

Rory wasn't right in bed when he found his windows begin to rattle, and in very short time the wind, rising, burst them in, and filled the room, lifting his bed from the floor, and laying it down again. All the whirlwinds of the world seemed to have gathered around the castle, all of them struggling to see which would have it. The trees in the woods for miles around seemed to be up-torn by the whirlwinds and flung against the castle, which quivered and shivered in every stone from the rafters to the foundation. All the broken branches of the wood, too, seemed to be banged into Rory's bedroom, where they banged and battered him as he lay, tossed about with the tossing of his bed. He surely thought the world had come to an end, and before morning must be blown from its foundations.

The morning came with the wind gone down,

and when the old man appeared, he asked Rory Og how he had fared last night.

Rory Og said he had the terriblest night in all his life; and that if he should live to be a very old man, he couldn't be bribed with the wealth of the world to pass such a night again.

Said the old man, "I am the Master of the Winds and this night is only a little foretaste of what's ahead of you, if you persist in following up and trying to find the Princess Suil-dubh."

Said Rory Og, "If the dangers are a thousand times as dangerous, and the terrors a thousand times as terrible, I'll never give up till I find and win her."

Said the Master of the Winds, "I admire your courage, and hope you will succeed. When you ride after the deer today, it will disappear in a cave in the mountain-side. If you follow far enough through that cave, you'll reach the land, Under-the-World, whose King is the father of Princess Suil-dubh. And it is only then that your greatest trials will begin. However, if you have faith and trust in Suil-dubh, who, I have reason to know, loves you well, you may yet succeed."

Rory Og thanked the Master of the Winds, bade

him good-by, mounted his horse, and set off. He hadn't gone a hundred yards when he raised again the deer he had been chasing, and followed it till it ran into a cave in the hillside. Rory galloped after it into the cave, and through it like the wind—his only light the fire that flashed from his horse's eyes. He rode far, and far, and very, very far; he rode long and long, and very, very long—and when he seemed to have been riding for four-and-twenty hours, he at length came out in the land, Under-the-World—a beautiful country, which he had never before seen nor heard tell of.

The deer was still before him, and at the same distance. He followed it far, and far over this lovely land, and when he was on the hilltop, the deer would be in the next hollow, and when he reached the hollow, the deer would be on the next hilltop. And so he went till, late that evening, he saw a great castle on a hillside far off. The deer headed straight for this castle, but disappeared at a ford just below it.

Rory Og crossed the ford and rode up to the castle. He found hanging from above the castle gate a great horn tipped with gold. Taking hold of this horn, he blew three blasts; and very soon a great, dark, ugly-looking gentleman appeared, frowning a frightful frown upon Rory, and demanding his business.

Rory said, "I am Rory Og O'Donnell, son of the King of Donegal. Several days ago, I saved the life of your daughter, the Princess Suil-dubh, when she was boating on the river Erne. In reward she granted me three wishes. One of my wishes was to win her. And to do that I have come through terrors and dangers from which men tried in vain to turn me. Now I am here to demand her as my wife."

The ugly, dark fellow when he heard this, frowned ten times more terribly and said, "If you have come through terrors and dangers to reach here, they are only a foretaste of what you have to go through before you win her. I advise you to turn yet before it is too late, and give her up."

Said Rory Og, "If the dangers were a thousand times more dangerous, and the terrors a thousand times more terrible, I'd gladly have them all and lose my life rather than give up the Princess Suil-dubh."

"Well," said the dark fellow, "if you are bent

on your death, what does it matter to me? I am King of Under-the-World, stepfather to three damsels, the youngest of whom is the Princess Suil-dubh. Ninety-nine champions, bewitched with her beauty, came here to claim her, but because, like you, they wouldn't turn aside, they faced the dangers, and lost their heads. Do you see a hundred spikes upon that castle wall; every spike, but one, having on it a man's head?"

"I see that," said Rory Og. And he shivered at the sight.

"Well," said the King of Under-the-World, "the hundredth spike is waiting for your head, if you fail to do any one of the three tasks which I'll put before you, and which you must perform before my daughter is won."

Said Rory Og bravely, "To win the beautiful Princess Suil-dubh, there are no tasks in all the world that I won't do, or die in attempting."

"Very well," said the King. "In the morning, I'll give you your first task."

He took in Rory Og, gave him his supper, and a soft bed that night. And in the morning, after Rory Og had breakfasted, the King appeared, asking him if he was ready for his first task.

"I'm ready," said Rory Og.

"Then come along with me," said the King. And he led him out into his courtyard, and showed him there seven stables, each holding seven hundred horses, seven hundred cows, seven hundred oxen and seven hundred asses. And the stables had not been cleaned out for seven years. The King said to Rory Og, "I want you today to clean out these stables. If before evening you haven't every one of them so clean that Princes might sup from the floors, without using a tablecloth, your head will go on the hundredth spike. Good-by."

And then the frowning fellow went off, leaving poor Rory Og looking at the task that was laid before him, and sadly shaking his head.

"Well, Rory Og, my fine fellow," Rory said to himself, "you made up your mind to face terrible things for the Princess Suil-dubh, but you never dreamed that such a task as this should be put before you."

But Rory Og was a brave fellow, and he said, "Even though man cannot do the task, I'll at least do my best before I die, and sure the best can do no more."

Throwing off his coat, he took up a graip (four-pronged fork), and went at his work with a will. But, behold you! For every graipful that Rory Og flung out of the door, seven graipfuls were flung in, through each of the seven doors of all the seven stables! And the more he flung out the worse was his task getting, and the higher were the heaps growing—till at length, throwing the graip from him, he sat down outside the door in despair.

That moment he heard a voice, the sweetest in all the world, saying, "Rory Og, my brave fellow, how is your work going?"

And looking up, who should he see standing by him but the Princess Suil-dubh! And her smile lit up the land.

"Oh!" said Rory. "I'm sorry to say I have found out that your advice not to try to win you was maybe the wisest that could have been given to mortal man."

"Then," said the Princess, "if yet you like to rue and go back, I can still save you."

"No!" said Rory Og. "I would a hundred times sooner die trying to win you, than live a joyless life without you. I'm heartily willing to lose my head for your sake."

265

"I'm proud of you, Rory Og," said the Princess Suil-dubh, "and perhaps I can help you with this task." Then she said, "Take all the graips from all the stables, and arrange them in rows."

Rory did this, and when he had a hundred graips ranged in rows, the Princess Suil-dubh just waved her hand, and the hundred graips of their own accord began to work. And for every graipful that each of them threw out of the door, seven hundred other graipfuls went along with them out of every one of the forty-nine doors—and in almost as short a time as I tell it, the stables were so clean that when the Princess took from her pocket a golden apple and rolled it across the floor, it took neither dirt, dust, nor stain!

"Now, Rory," she said, "at least you have a third of me won—but on the peril of your life, don't say it was I who helped you."

Rory, in joy, didn't know how to thank the Princess. But she said, "Rory, do not mention thanks. A thousand times as much I would gladly do for you." Then she went away.

Rory now sauntered around, singing and whistling light-heartedly till evening came on, and the

King came out, smiling at the thought of having poor Rory's head on the spike.

But when the King walked into the stables, and saw every one of them so clean that Princes might eat off the floors without a tablecloth, he reddened and blackened with rage, and said, "You have done your task, you villain! But I'm sure you haven't done it by fair means!"

"As fair they are as you deserve, anyhow," said Rory Og.

"Never mind, you rascal!" said the King. "I'll give you a task tomorrow that you'll surely not do. And then your head will be mine!"

"I'll not worry," said Rory. "Let each day do its own deeds."

When the King went back to the castle, he sought out his wife, and asked her what was the Princess Suil-dubh doing today.

"She was in her room carding wool all day," said his wife.

Very well and good. After breakfast in the morning, the King came to Rory Og again, and told him to come along, till he'd give him his second task. And Rory went with him.

He took Rory Og into the courtyard, and

showed him the seven stables that were each a mile long, and pointed out that during the night the wind had come and stripped every straw off the thatched roofs of the stables.

"Your task today," the King said, "is to thatch these seven stables that are each a mile long. You must thatch them with the feathers of the birds of the air, no two feathers to be of the same kind, or from the same bird. If you haven't that done before night, your head will sit on the hundredth spike. Good-by."

And the King went off.

Poor Rory looked at the seven miles of stables and thought how they must be thatched before night with the feathers of the birds—and then sadly shook his head, saying, "Great terrors and dangers were prophesied for me, if I pursued the Princess Suil-dubh, but I did not think that anything so terrible as this would be put before me— a task that no mortal man could do. However," said my brave Rory, "I'll do my best, and the best can do no more."

So he immediately began galloping after every bird he could see. For three hours the poor fellow nigh broke both his neck and legs running hither and thither and yonder after the birds. And when he could run no longer, he had got just three feathers in the heart of his hand. The poor fellow looked at the three feathers in the heart of his hand, and looked at the roofs of the seven stables that were each a mile long, and thought how he'd lose his head if he hadn't them thatched before night with the feathers of the birds of the air, no two feathers of the same kind, or from the same bird—and he sat down in despair.

All at once he heard the sweetest voice in all the world saying, "Rory, how is your task getting done today?"

And looking up he saw, standing by him, the beautiful Princess Suil-dubh. And her smile lit all the land.

"Oh!" Rory said. "The wisest man would have been well advised to have taken your advice, and not come after you. I was prepared to undergo any terror or danger for your sake, but I never dreamed that such terrible tasks as this would be put before me."

Said the Princess: "Rory, it isn't yet too late to rue. I think I can still save your life, and send you back, if you will."

"No! No!" said Rory. "Sooner a hundred times would I lose my head trying to win you, than live a life of misery without you."

The Princess Suil-dubh then said, "Well, Rory, I'll do what I can to help you."

Putting her hand in her pocket, she took out a little golden whistle and blew on it three times. Immediately she did so, Rory saw what he thought were the ends of the world coming toward him—but instead it was flocks of birds from all the world coming over the horizon—birds of all sorts, and all sizes, from the woods and the scrugs, and the lakes and the wild seashore, birds from the marshes, and birds from the meadows, and larks from the blue, blue skies—from under the world, and over the world they were coming, in flocks and droves and shoals.

When they arrived at the castle they flew hither and thither over the stables, each bird dropping from its wing a feather. And every feather fell into its own place on the stable roofs—till, in almost as short a time as I tell you, the whole seven stables that were each a mile long, were thatched with the feathers of the birds of the air, no two feathers of the same kind, or from the same bird!

And the Princess Suil-dubh said, "Well, Rory, you have now two-thirds of me won."

And Rory, filled with joy and gratitude, didn't know how to thank the Princess Suil-dubh.

She said, "No thanks I need, Rory; for I would do a thousand times as much for you. But on your peril, don't tell that I helped you." And then she went away.

When the King came out in the evening he was smiling with pleasure at the thought of having Rory's head so soon now. But when his eye fell on the stables, and he saw them thatched with the feathers of the birds of the air, no two feathers being of the same kind or from the same bird, he went red and black with wrath. And he said, "You rascal, I don't know how you have done this task, which I thought impossible for man to perform. But I'm sure you haven't done it by fair means!"

"As fair they are as you deserve, anyhow," said Rory.

"All right," said the King, "you have done these two tasks; but tomorrow I'll give you one you'll not do, and then I'll have your head surely!"

"I'll not worry," said Rory. "Let each day do its own deeds."

And when the King went into the castle again, he asked his wife what had the Princess Suil-dubh been doing today. And his wife replied, "She has been spinning in her room all day."

Next morning, after breakfast, the King took Rory with him to a pond at the foot of his lawn. In the middle of the pond was a green island, and on the island grew a tree, five hundred feet high. For the first four-hundred-and-ninety-five feet from the ground, there was neither branch, knot, nor knob on the trunk of the tree—nor rough bark either—but it was smooth and oily. The topmost five feet of the tree threw out branches and in them was a crane's nest. The King said, "There are three eggs in that crane's nest which I want for my supper tonight. You must fetch them for me without crack or break, or else I'll have your head. Good-by."

And the King went away.

Rory looked at this tree that was smooth and slippery for the first four-hundred-and-ninety-five feet; and then sadly shook his head. But the brave fellow said, "Sure I'll do my best, and the best can do no more."

And, throwing off his coat, he began to try to climb the tree. But he could get neither hold nor grasp on it. Six inches he couldn't raise himself up but six inches he would instantly slip back. And after Rory Og had been three hours climbing the tree, his feet were still on the ground—and the crane's nest as far from him as ever. In despair at length he sat down, with his head resting dolefully between his hands.

All at once he heard the sweetest voice in all the world, and looking up saw standing by him the beautiful Princess Suil-dubh, and her smile lit up the land.

She said, "Rory, have you robbed the crane's nest yet?"

"Oh! No! No!" Rory replied. "I thought the tasks which he gave me yesterday and the day before were the most difficult that could be put before man, but this day's task is surely more difficult still. Wise would have been the man who heeded your warning, when you asked me not to try to win you."

Said the Princess Suil-dubh: "If you rue not

273

taking my warning, I may have the power to save you still, and send you home unhurt."

"No! No!" said Rory. "A thousand times I'd rather lose my life trying to win you, than lead a lonely life without you."

"Then, Rory," said the Princess, "maybe I can help you in this third task also."

"Oh! No! No!" said Rory. "You might clean out the stables for me, and thatch them likewise— but by no chance in the world could you climb this terrible tree."

The Princess only smiled, and, resting her left foot on a rock, began taking it apart in all its little bones, to Rory's astonishment. Out of it she took four-hundred-and-ninety-five little bones, and gave them to Rory, saying, "These will make for you steps to the top of the tree. Every little bone will stick to the tree wherever you place it and make a step. As you go up, keep sticking a bone to the tree for every foot you go, and in that way you will have a ladder that will carry you to the top. When you have got the eggs in your pocket, and are coming down again, be sure, dear Rory, not to forget any single bone. If any bone be left we could never get it again, because I never can use my foot, in this way, twice for the same purpose."

With all his heart Rory thanked her and promised her that he would leave no bone behind as he came down.

When Rory put one little bone to the tree it stuck there, making a step for him, and then he put a second bone a foot higher up, it also stuck, making a step—and so on till the bones brought him to the branches above. There he pocketed the crane's eggs, and started down again, gathering the bones with him as he descended. Reaching the earth he gave the full of his hands of bones back to the Princess, who began putting them into her foot again.

But, behold you! when she came to the end of them, she found he had only given her four-hundred-and-ninety-four bones, and there was one bone still missing—the top joint of her little toe, which bone poor Rory had unfortunately forgotten at the very top.

When Rory found what he had done he was loud in his lamentations, and said he would sooner a thousand times have lost his life than that she should lose, for him, the joint from her little toe.

"Oh, Rory," said the Princess, "for your sake I would gladly lose not only the joint of my little toe, but my life itself along with it. But unfortunately my stepfather, who has all along suspected me of helping you, will now find out our secret. At bedtime every night he washes the feet of my sisters and myself, and when he comes to mine, and finds the joint of my little toe gone, he will know all—and will have the lives of both of us."

Poor Rory Og was in fearful distress when he heard this.

"Losing my own life, I don't mind," he said, "but that your life should be lost for me is what I cannot get over."

"Well, Rory Og," said the beautiful Princess, "I wouldn't mind losing my life if it saved yours. But at the same time, there's just one chance for our escape."

"What's that?" said Rory Og.

She said, "The King always washes the feet of my sisters before he washes mine. While he is engaged with my sisters is our only chance. You must then go quickly to the stables, and saddle for us the swiftest horse there."

"How shall I know the swiftest horse?" said Rory Og.

Said the Princess: "You must pass the first six stables by, and go into the seventh. When you enter there you'll first find a row of three-hundred-and-sixty-five white horses. Don't take any of them, for white horses are weak horses on a long run. You will next see a row of three-hundred-and sixty-five chestnut horses. Don't take any of them, because chestnut horses aren't swift horses on a long run. You'll next find a row of three-hundred-and-sixty-five black horses. Take one of them, because black horses are the strongest, and the swiftest, and the most lasting horses on a long run. Don't take the first, and don't take the second, and don't take the third—don't take any of the black horses till you come to the last of the three-hundred-and-sixty-five. The three-hundred-and sixty-fifth is the strongest and swiftest, and most lasting horse in the stables. Saddle and bridle him, and bring him under my window."

Rory promised to do this, and the Princess went away to prepare for her flight.

When Rory that evening presented the King with the three eggs from the crane's nest, the King was in ten times greater wrath than he had ever been before. He said, "You rascal, you have done this third task; but you haven't done it by fair means, I am sure!"

"As fair they are as you deserve, anyhow," said Rory.

The King said, "I must keep my word. If you are still alive by tomorrow morning, come to me and you'll have the Princess."

"All right," said Rory Og. And he went away.

Rory, that evening, listened carefully till he heard the King call the eldest daughter to have her feet washed. Then off to the stables he ran, passing six of them, and entering the seventh. The first thing he found was a row of three-hundred-and-sixty-five white horses. But he passed them by, because white horses are weak horses on a long run. Next were a row of three-hundred-and-sixty-five chestnut horses. But he passed them by, for chestnut horses are not swift horses on a long run. Next was a row of three-hundred-and-sixty-five black horses. He didn't pass them by, for black horses are the strongest, and swiftest, and

278

most lasting, on a long run. He didn't take the first, and he didn't take the second, and he didn't take the third—didn't take any till he came to the last horse in the stable. Him he saddled and bridled, led him out under the window of the Princess, who, jumping down, mounted behind Rory Og—and both of them went away like the wind.

Now, before the Princess left, she had cut an apple into four quarters. One quarter was laid at her bedside, and one by her dressing-table, one at the threshold of her room, and one in the hall that led toward the King's room. As soon as the King had finished washing the feet of his two older daughters, he called for the Princess Suil-dubh, asking, "Are you coming to have your feet washed?"

The quarter-apple that was by her bedside answered, "I'm coming as soon as I have taken my stockings off."

After a while he called to the Princess again, asking if she was coming to have her feet washed. And the apple by the dressing-table answered, "I'm coming as soon as I have my hair put up."

After a while the King called to the Princess

again, saying, "Are you coming to have your feet washed?" And the apple that was on the threshold of her room said, "I'm coming as soon as I close my room-door."

After a while the King again called, asking if she was coming to have her feet washed. And the apple in the hall said, "I'm coming along the hall."

And when after a while he called again, asking if the Princess was coming to have her feet washed he got no answer. He jumped up at once, suspecting there was something wrong, ran to her room, and found her gone. Then he ran to Rory Og's room, and found him gone, too. And immediately he saddled the second swiftest horse in the stables, and rode like the wind after the flying pair.

When Rory Og and the Princess had ridden far and far, and Rory Og thought they were safe, the Princess said, "Rory Og, I surely feel the heat of the King's hot, angry breath burning my back. Look behind and see if he's pursuing."

And Rory Og, looking behind, cried out, "Yes! yes! he's pursuing. He'll soon be on us, and our lives are surely lost."

"Not yet, Rory," said the Princess. "Look into the horse's left ear and see what is there."

"There is a drop of water here," said Rory, looking into the horse's left ear.

Said the Princess: "Throw that drop of water over your left shoulder, and see what'll happen."

Rory did so and immediately there was a great rushing river flowing across their tracks—between them and the pursuing King. And when the King came to the banks of the river, he had to search for a boat, and employ men to man it. Then Rory and the Princess had a good start again, and Rory at length thought they were safe.

But again the Princess cried out, "Rory, I surely feel the heat of the King's hot, angry breath burning my back. Look behind and find if he is following."

Rory Og looked behind, and there, sure enough, saw the King again in sight. Fire was flashing from his eyes, and he was drawing his sword to slay them, as his horse at every bound was nearing the horse of Rory and the Princess.

"He is overtaking us," said Rory Og, "and our lives are surely lost."

"Not yet, Rory," said the Princess. "Look into the horse's right ear, and see if anything is there."

"Nothing is here but the seed of a tree," said Rory.

"Then throw the seed over your right shoulder, Rory, and see what will happen," said the Princess.

Rory did this. And immediately he did so a great wood that was twenty miles every way, and so thick and so high, that a bird couldn't fly through it or over it, sprang up behind them, between them and the pursuing King.

And when the King reached the wood, he had to search for men with axes and saws to cut a way for him through the wood.

Then Rory and the Princess had gone so far that Rory thought they were surely safe.

But at length the Princess said, "Rory, I surely feel the heat of the King's hot angry breath burning my back. Look behind, and see if he is following."

Rory did so, and saw the King following, and now riding right close upon them. Fire was flashing from his eyes, and he had his drawn sword raised in the air to cut them down. And in another few bounds his horse would surely be upon them.

Rory said, "We are surely lost this time."

"Not yet, not yet, Rory," said the Princess. "Look between the horse's two ears. and see if anything is there."

"I see nothing here, but a little drop of pitch," said Rory.

Said the Princess: "Throw that over your head and see what will happen."

Rory took the drop of pitch, and threw it backward over his head. Immediately he did so, there was rolling behind them, between them and the King, a river of boiling pitch. But in such terrible rage was the King, that he never paused or halted or tightened a rein, but plunged into the river of boiling pitch, where himself and his horse went under, and the river rolled over them forever!

Then on and on rode Rory and his beautiful Princess, through the cavern in the mountain, and out on the other side. They swept past the castle of the Master of the Winds, who was waving to them from a tower—but no wind stirred even the grass-blades. They swept past the castle of the

Master of the Rains, who was waving to them from his tower—and no raindrop fell on the fields. They next swept past the castle of the Master of the Snows, who was waving to them from his tower—but no sprinkle of snow did they find.

Halt or pause they did not, nor draw rein, till they crossed the bridge over the Erne, and entered the country of Rory's father, and rode to his father's castle in Donegal.

His father and his mother had given up Rory Og as dead. Both of them ran out, overjoyed, when they heard he was come home again. But far greater was their joy when they found that he had with him the Princess Suil-dubh—the handsomest damsel ever seen at that or any other court. Rory Og and the Princess were married. Rory's father gave a feast, which lasted twenty-one days and twenty-one nights, and the last day and night were as full of fun and merriment as the first. Rory Og soon reigned in his father's kingdom with his beautiful young Queen.

And happy and well they lived ever after.